Scott Foresman

Ties Through Time

What things do
we do together
in the same
special way?

Hear the Cheers
by Diane Hoyt-Goldsmith

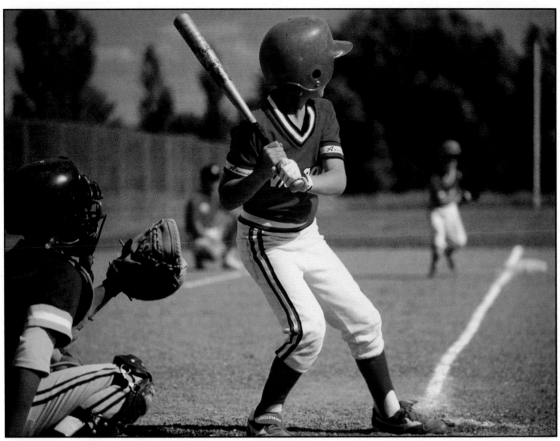

The batter waits for the pitch in a baseball game.

What can you play with a ball and a bat? You can play baseball. When the bat hits the ball, the fans cheer loudly. The ball sails clear out of the park. It's a home run!

There are nine players on the team. The only gear the batter needs is a helmet to cover the head and ears. The best time each year is when baseball teams compete in the World Series. Clearly, baseball is still one of our favorite sports.

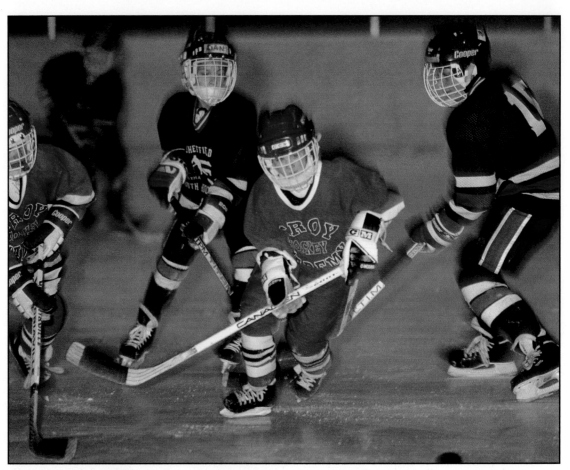
Players race for the puck in a hockey game.

What can you play with a stick and a puck? You can play hockey. Players skate quickly and smoothly over the ice. The goalie stands near the net. Hockey players need to put on lots of gear. The game is rough, but the players have no fear. They pass and steer the puck with their sticks. They shoot the puck into the net. Score! The crowd cheers.

In the 1850s, lacrosse was a favorite game of the Sioux.

What game can you play with a ball and a stick? You can play lacrosse. Native Americans played lacrosse hundreds of years ago, and it is still popular.

For them it was more than a game. It helped them to be better deer hunters. It was also a way to solve problems peacefully. The team that won the game also won the argument. Native Americans had a good idea when they thought up the game of lacrosse.

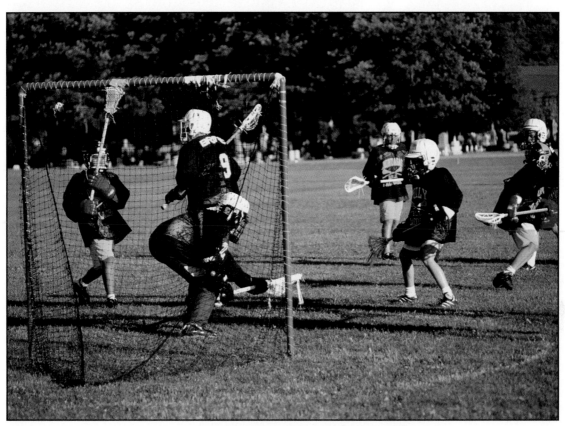

Members of the Onondaga Nation, New York, play lacrosse today.

In lacrosse, players cannot touch the ball with their hands. They easily throw and catch the ball with the net on their sticks. When the ball goes into the goal, a point is scored. Then you can hear the cheers.

The Great Ball Game

A Muskogee Story

retold by
Joseph Bruchac

illustrated by
Susan L. Roth

Long ago the Birds and Animals had a great argument.

"We who have wings are better than you," said
the Birds.

"That is not so," the Animals replied. "We who have teeth are better."

The two sides argued back and forth. Their quarrel went on and on, until it seemed they would go to war because of it.

Then Crane, the leader of the Birds, and Bear, the leader of the Animals, had an idea.

"Let us have a ball game," Crane said. "The first side to score a goal will win the argument."

"This idea is good," said Bear. "The side that loses will have to accept the penalty given by the other side."

So they walked and flew to a field, and there they divided up into two teams.

This is how Bat came to be accepted as an Animal. He was allowed to set the penalty for the Birds.

"You Birds," Bat said, "must leave this land for half of each year."

So it is that the Birds fly south each winter.
And every day at dusk Bat still comes flying to see
if the Animals need him to play ball.

About the Author
Joseph Bruchac

Joseph Bruchac enjoyed the Native American stories he learned as a child. He first told them to his sons. Then he began retelling them in books and performing them for others. Today he is a performing storyteller. Mr. Bruchac's Abenaki Indian name is Sozap.

About the Illustrator
Susan L. Roth

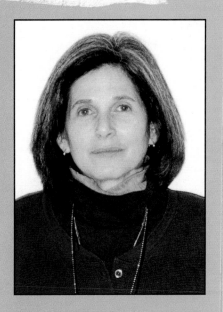

Susan L. Roth uses torn and cut paper to create her work. In *The Great Ball Game,* she used papers from around the world to make her pictures. Ms. Roth has also written children's books.

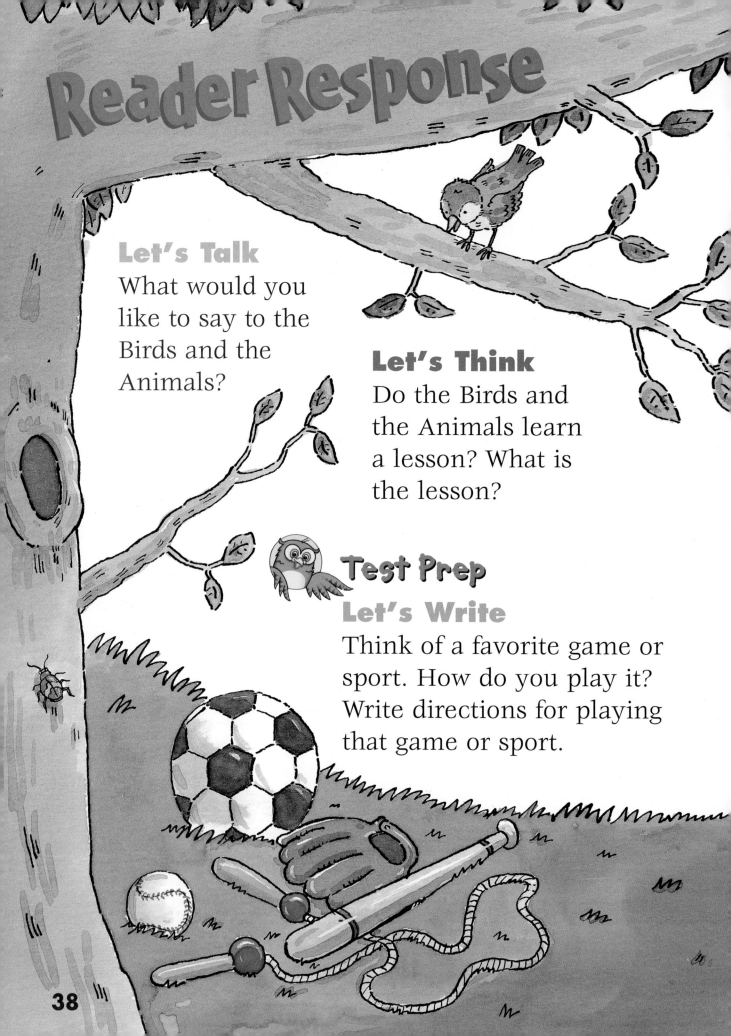

Reader Response

Let's Talk
What would you like to say to the Birds and the Animals?

Let's Think
Do the Birds and the Animals learn a lesson? What is the lesson?

Test Prep
Let's Write
Think of a favorite game or sport. How do you play it? Write directions for playing that game or sport.

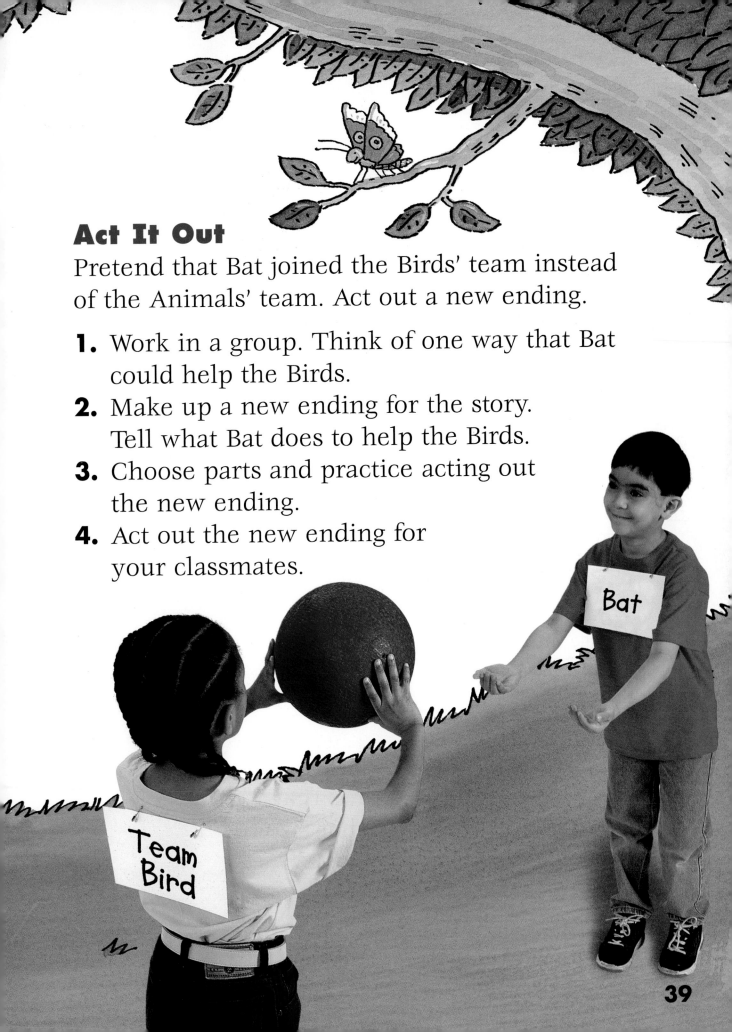

Act It Out

Pretend that Bat joined the Birds' team instead of the Animals' team. Act out a new ending.

1. Work in a group. Think of one way that Bat could help the Birds.
2. Make up a new ending for the story. Tell what Bat does to help the Birds.
3. Choose parts and practice acting out the new ending.
4. Act out the new ending for your classmates.

Language Arts

Adjectives

An **adjective** describes a noun. An adjective may tell how many, what size, or what shape.

Ten animals are on the playground.

Kick the **round** ball.

The **little** rabbit jumps rope.

adjective	noun
Ten	animals
round	ball
little	rabbit

Talk

Talk about the picture. Describe what you see. Use words that describe how many, what size, and what shape.

Write

Write the sentences. Circle the adjectives.

1. Who throws a big ball in the round hoop?
2. The little bear kicks the ball.
3. The animals use two balls.

Write sentences about the playground at your school. Use adjectives that tell how many, what size, or what shape.

Birthday Joy

by Anne Sibley O'Brien

When you have your birthday, is there a wonderful cake with candles? Do your friends join in to sing "Happy Birthday" to you? Do you get toys?

All over the world, boys and girls have different ways of having a joyful birthday. Has anyone ever told you about this?

In Germany, the birthday girl or boy has a beautiful birthday candle. The mother or father lights this important candle to point out the child's age. On each birthday, the candle burns down to the next number.

In Mexico, the birthday boy or girl might get a piñata. The father takes his child to the market to look about at all the different piñatas. The child might choose a colorful bird, a beautiful horse, or a dog with pointed ears. It is hard to make a choice!

Later, friends join the birthday child for a wonderful party. Each boy and girl tries to break the piñata. When it cracks, candy and toys spill about for everyone to enjoy!

In Israel, the birthday girl or boy gets a beautiful crown of flowers. The mother places the royal crown on her child's head. The child looks very important!

Then the birthday girl or boy sits in a special chair. The father is careful to raise the chair once for each year. Friends make noise and dance about as the chair goes up and down.

Now you have been told! All over the world, boys and girls enjoy their birthdays in many different ways.

The Best Older Sister

by Sook Nyul Choi

illustrated by Yoshi Miyake

1. No Time for Sunhi

Sunhi dragged her feet as she walked home from school. Her grandmother, Halmoni, had always waited for Sunhi outside the schoolyard with a delicious snack. Together they would walk home. Sunhi would tell Halmoni all about her day at school.

But everything changed for Sunhi when her little brother, Kiju, was born.

"Oh, hello, Sunhi," said Mrs. Lee, looking up finally. "We just stopped by to see Kiju.

"How adorable your little brother is! I can hardly believe he will be a year old next week."

"Halmoni told us that it is a Korean custom to have a big party on a baby's first birthday," said Mrs. Stone. "You must be so excited."

Sunhi managed a polite smile.

"It is so wonderful to have a boy in the family," said Mrs. Lee.

Sunhi was tired of all the fuss everyone made over this baby. She did not think he was so interesting. She wished one of these visitors would adopt him and take him away.

"Can I have my bear back? That is still mine, isn't it?"

Sunhi snatched it and ran to her room.

Everything was different with Kiju around. Even her room was not her own anymore. It was full of baby diapers and baby toys. It smelled like baby powder.

"How happy you must be to have a little brother!" everyone said to Sunhi.

"Isn't it wonderful to be a big sister now?" they asked.

But it did not seem so wonderful to Sunhi. Now her parents had even less time to talk to her and play with her in the evenings.

Most of all, Sunhi missed spending time with Halmoni. When Halmoni wasn't with Kiju, she was busy doing things for him.

Just yesterday Sunhi had caught Halmoni sewing secretly in her room. Sunhi saw the beautiful blue silk.

She knew that Halmoni must be making something for Kiju to wear on his birthday.

"What is so special about this little baby, anyway?" Sunhi wondered. "Why is it so important to have a boy? Wasn't I good enough?" Sunhi sobbed.

In the box was a royal blue silk Korean dress. It had rainbow-colored sleeves and butterflies embroidered on the front. Sunhi loved it.

"This is for you to wear on Kiju's birthday," said Halmoni. "I was afraid you saw it last night when you came to say good night.

"These other two are for your best friends, Jenny and Robin. Open them and see if you think they will like them."

58

Jenny's was peach-colored with white rosebuds embroidered on the front. Robin's was yellow with tiny blue birds embroidered on the sleeves. Sunhi knew that her friends would love these.

"Halmoni, these are so pretty. It must have taken you a very long time to make them!" said Sunhi.

"Well, luckily Kiju is a good baby. He sleeps a lot. I am sorry I haven't taken you to school and picked you up. I have missed that.

"You are special to me. It is just that babies are so helpless and need a lot of care. Just like when you were a baby," said Halmoni.

"Did people come and visit and make such a big fuss over me?" asked Sunhi.

"Oh, even more!" said Halmoni. "What a fuss we all made!

"Don't you remember the pictures of your first birthday? I was in Korea, but your parents sent me a big batch of pictures of you every week.

"For your birthday, I made you an outfit and mailed it to your mother."

"I remember those pictures," said Sunhi.

"Now that you are a big sister," said Halmoni, "I thought you could host Kiju's birthday party.

"You, Jenny, and Robin can decorate the birthday table and host together. Why don't you invite them over? We can give them their presents," said Halmoni.

Sunhi nodded.

"Okay, I'll ask them to come home with me tomorrow," she said. "Where is Kiju?"

Halmoni smiled. "I think he is sleeping. Let's go see."

3. A Bad Older Sister

Halmoni and Sunhi walked to Sunhi's parents' room. They peered into Kiju's crib.

Kiju was wide awake and playing happily with his feet. He was a peaceful, handsome baby.

"Kiju is lucky to have a big sister like you," said Halmoni.

"Soon he will be walking and talking. He will follow you all around. You will have to teach him to be smart and kind just like you."

Sunhi's face turned red.

"Halmoni, I was stupid and mean. Sometimes I wanted to be an only child again. I have been a bad older sister," said Sunhi.

"Sunhi, that is all right," said Halmoni. "It is hard to get used to having a baby in the house.

"Sometimes we wish things had not changed. But that doesn't mean we are bad. I know that you love Kiju very much. I know you are going to be the best older sister."

Sunhi watched Kiju. She promised herself that she would give him the best first birthday party ever.

"What is Kiju's birthday outfit like?" asked Sunhi.

"It is just a silk outfit much like the one you wore," said Sunhi's mother, walking into the room.

"He is not wearing an extra-special outfit? He isn't more special and important because he is a boy?" asked Sunhi.

"Of course not! You are both equally special," said Sunhi's mother.

She hugged Sunhi.

Halmoni took Sunhi's hand in her own. She said, "Is your right eye more special and important than your left eye?"

Halmoni had lots of funny sayings like this, but Sunhi understood.

About the Author
Sook Nyul Choi

"I have always loved books," says Sook Nyul Choi. "As a young girl growing up in Korea, I loved collecting books." Ms. Choi began writing poems and stories as a girl. She found that writing let her share her "thoughts, ideas, and feelings."

Seeing A NEW Sister

by E. Alma Flagg

Baby sister doesn't know
What's going on at all;
How will I ever play with her?
She is so soft and small.

How can I even talk to her?
She only sleeps and sleeps;
But I suppose we'll get along—
They say she's here for keeps.

Reader Response

Let's Talk

Have you ever felt left out like Sunhi? What did you do about it?

Let's Think

Halmoni says, "Is your right eye more special and important than your left eye?" What does she mean?

Test Prep

Let's Write

Pretend that you are Sunhi. Write in your journal about your day. Tell about the lessons you learned.

Make an Invitation

Sunhi will host Kiju's party. Pretend that you will be the host of a party. Make an invitation for your party.

1. Think of a party you would like to host.
2. Make an invitation.
   Write
   - The day of the party
   - The time
   - Where it will be
   - The reason for the party
3. Draw pictures.
4. Share your invitation with classmates.

You Are Invited

A Party
for: Sarah
day: Saturday, August 2
time: 12:00 p.m.
where: 703 Elm
reason: 9th Birthday

Language Arts

Adjectives

An **adjective** describes a noun. An adjective may tell how something looks, feels, sounds, tastes, or smells.

Grandpa mixes the **crisp, green** salad.

The baby gives a **loud** cry.

The girl drinks **sour** lemonade.

Talk

Tell about the picture. Use adjectives that tell how something looks, feels, sounds, tastes, or smells.

GORDON FAMILY REUNION

Write

Write these sentences. Use adjectives from the box to finish each sentence.

It was a _____ day. Everyone came to the picnic. We had a lot to eat. The _____ hamburgers were good. The games were fun. We played with a _____ ball.

adjectives		
salty	soft	hot
round	blue	sunny

Write your own sentences about a party. Leave spaces for adjectives. Ask a friend to write an adjective in each space.

Treasure Pie

by Toby Speed   illustrated by Susan Swan

Moose read the note.

Dear Moose,
   Will you come for breakfast today? My pen pal, Bear, is here to visit. She is making her special dish called Treasure Pie. Come to my house at 9:00. Bring bread.
            Your friend,
            Dog

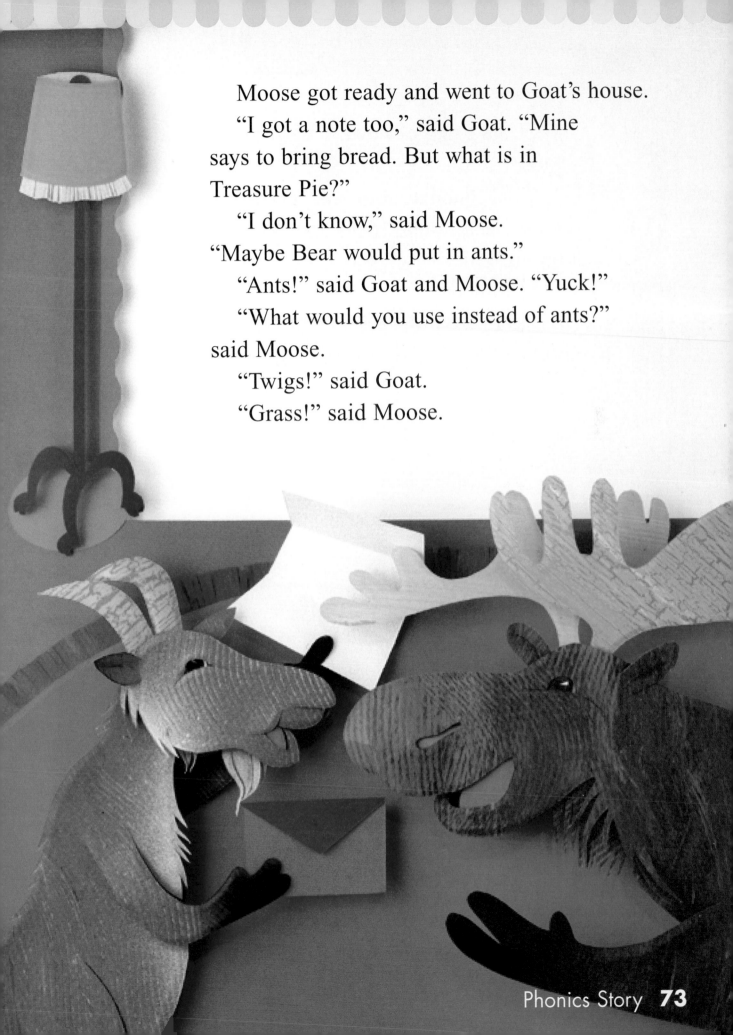

Moose got ready and went to Goat's house.

"I got a note too," said Goat. "Mine says to bring bread. But what is in Treasure Pie?"

"I don't know," said Moose. "Maybe Bear would put in ants."

"Ants!" said Goat and Moose. "Yuck!"

"What would you use instead of ants?" said Moose.

"Twigs!" said Goat.

"Grass!" said Moose.

"Let's bring our own Treasure Pie," said Moose.

Goat found a large pot. Moose picked grass. Goat found twigs and spread them out on the table.

"I'll be the washer," said Moose. He began to wash the grass.

"Go ahead," said Goat. "I'll be the cutter."

Moose turned on the oven. "Now for the bread," he said.

"I'm a good baker and mixer," said Goat.

Goat measured and mixed. He put the pan in the oven and set the timer. Soon the bread was ready.

"You are a very good baker," said Moose. Then they got ready to go to Dog's house.

"Hello!" shouted Dog. "Moose and Goat, meet Bear."

"It's a pleasure," said Bear. "I hope you enjoy my Treasure Pie."

"What's in it?" asked Goat and Moose.

"Apples!" said Bear.

"Apples?" said Goat. "Not ants?"

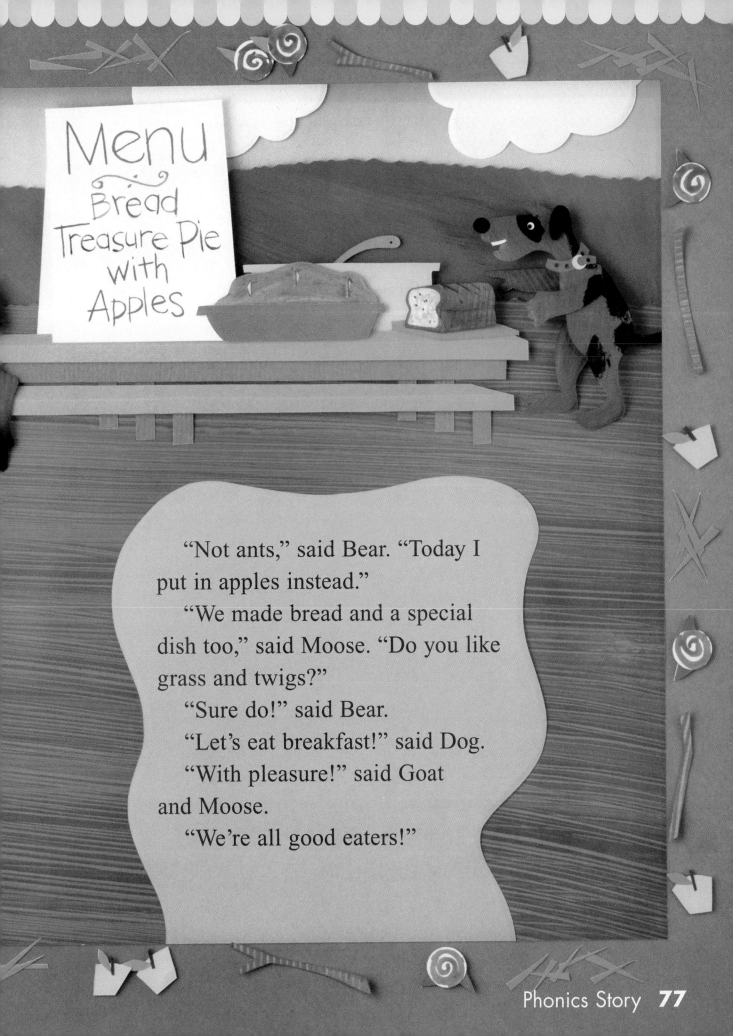

Menu
Bread
Treasure Pie
with
Apples

"Not ants," said Bear. "Today I put in apples instead."

"We made bread and a special dish too," said Moose. "Do you like grass and twigs?"

"Sure do!" said Bear.

"Let's eat breakfast!" said Dog.

"With pleasure!" said Goat and Moose.

"We're all good eaters!"

BRUNO
the Baker

by Lars Klinting

Who is that knocking on Bruno's window?
It's Felix. He has a present for Bruno.
Today is Bruno's birthday.

Bruno loves Felix's flowers. He wonders
if Felix would like to stay for some
birthday cake.

Well, first we have to make it!

Here is Bruno's kitchen. He has lots
of pots and pans. Bruno's grandma gave
them to him.

She was a good cook.

What are Bruno and Felix looking for?

Aha! Felix found it—Grandma's cookbook.

Bruno and Felix check the cupboard to see if they have all the ingredients for the cake recipe. They do. Now it's time to get started.

First Bruno melts the butter in a pan.

Next he takes out
the bread crumbs,

a basting brush,

and a cake pan.

Bruno brushes the inside of the cake pan with some of the melted butter. Then Felix pours some bread crumbs into the pan and shakes it so that the bread crumbs stick to the butter. Bruno turns on the oven.

Now it's time to take out the

sugar,   eggs,   and Bruno's favorite
                                            old bowl.

Bruno cracks the eggs into the bowl. Felix is
a good helper. He adds the sugar.

After Bruno stirs together the sugar and eggs, he takes out the electric mixer.

He beats the eggs and sugar until they are fluffy and almost white. Bruno loves this part. Felix thinks it's too noisy.

Bruno is now ready to mix the

baking soda,

confectioners' sugar,

and flour.

He blends them together in a small bowl.

Felix sets aside the mixing spoon

and the milk.

Bruno pours the milk and the rest of the melted butter into the big bowl with the egg and sugar mixture. Then Felix adds the contents of the small bowl.

Bruno follows the recipe directions carefully. The kitchen is getting a little messy but that's okay.

After Bruno and Felix blend the mixture well, they pour the batter into the cake pan. The cake is ready to bake in the oven.

Bruno wears his oven mitts so he won't get burned.

Felix sets the cake timer. Then Bruno and Felix sit in front of the oven.

The oven has a glass window and a light so they can watch the cake bake.

Pretty soon the kitchen is warm and cozy.

After sitting for a while Bruno and Felix decide to clean up. "Look at the mess we made. We better get to work," says Bruno.

Bruno and Felix wash the dishes while the cake is baking. The kitchen is soon tidy again.

The cake is done. Bruno takes it out of the
oven and lets it cool for a little while.

After it cools, Felix covers the cake with
a doily and places a large plate on top of
the doily.

Then Bruno slips one hand under the cake
pan and holds on to the top as he flips
the cake over. Bruno wiggles the pan a bit
and it comes off. And just look at that cake!
It's perfect!

Now Bruno and Felix take out

a tablecloth,

a pitcher of juice,

two glasses,

two plates,

two napkins,

and a knife to cut the cake.

Ding-dong!

Just as they finish setting the table
the doorbell rings.

Who can that be?

Happy birthday to you.
Happy birthday to you.
Happy birthday, dear Bruno . . .

"Hurry, Felix! We'll need more plates and glasses!" says Bruno.

Bruno is happy that his friends have arrived just in time for cake. Everyone agrees that the birthday cake is delicious.

Bruno couldn't have done it without his little buddy, Felix.

What do you think Bruno gets as a present?

A beautiful new mixing bowl!

About the Author
Lars Klinting

Lars Klinting was born in Sweden. He is not only an author but an illustrator. Mr. Klinting has written other Bruno books. He is busy creating another book about Bruno, who can do so many things!

BRUNO'S CAKE

8" x 2" cake pan

$5\frac{1}{8}$ tablespoons butter or margarine

1 tablespoon plain bread crumbs, finely ground

2 large eggs

1 cup granulated sugar

$1\frac{1}{2}$ cups all-purpose flour, sifted

$1\frac{1}{2}$ teaspoons baking soda

1 tablespoon confectioners' sugar (or 1 teaspoon vanilla extract)

$\frac{1}{2}$ cup milk

1. Preheat oven to 350° F.

2. Melt the butter in a pan over a low flame.

3. Brush the cake pan with some of the melted butter.

4. Pour the bread crumbs in the cake pan. Shake it carefully so that the crumbs stick to the sides of the pan.

5. Beat the eggs and sugar together in a large bowl until the mixture is fluffy.

6. Combine the flour, baking soda, and confectioners' sugar (or vanilla extract) in a small bowl. Stir well. Make sure there are no lumps.

7. Blend milk, remaining butter, and combined flour, baking soda, and confectioners' sugar with the egg and sugar mixture in the large bowl. Mix until smooth.

8. Pour the batter into the cake pan. Bake for 35 minutes. Stick a toothpick in the center of the cake. If it comes out clean, the cake is done.

9. Let the cake sit for one hour.

To serve the cake as Bruno did: Place a paper doily on top of cake and then place a large plate facedown over the doily. Slip one hand under the cake pan and hold on to the top as you flip the cake over. Lightly wiggle the pan free. Sprinkle the top of the cake with confectioners' sugar.

Yield: 8 pieces of cake.

Reader Response

Let's Talk
Would you like
to plan a party?
Why or why not?

Let's Think
Why is it
important to
make sure you
have everything
before you bake
a cake?

Test Prep
Let's Write
Bruno makes a cake.
What can you make?
Write directions for
someone to follow.

Make a Plan

Today is Bruno's birthday.
Have a party for him. What will you need to do?
Make a plan.

1. Think about your party. What will it be like?

2. Write these questions. Then write your answers below each question.

- **What will we do?**
- **What will we eat?**
- **How will I decorate?**
- **What other ideas do I have?**

3. Compare your plan with a classmate's plan. You may want to share some ideas!

Language Arts

Writing with Adjectives

You can use **adjectives** to describe the nouns in your sentences. Adjectives make your sentences clearer and more interesting.

The baker wears a hat.

The **happy** baker wears a **tall** hat.

His helper finds a pan.

His **little** helper finds a **big** pan.

Talk

Pretend you are the cook in the picture. Describe your kitchen and what you are making. Use the list of adjectives.

adjectives		
cozy	sweet	fluffy
messy	white	lumpy
clean	hot	smooth
cold	tasty	large

Write

Write these sentences. Add adjectives to make the sentences clearer and more interesting.

The baker makes a cake in the kitchen. He mixes the batter with a spoon. He pours the batter into a pan. When the cake is finished, he will spread frosting on it.

Write your own sentences about a favorite food. Use adjectives. Ask others if they would like to try your food.

Paul Goes to the Ball

by Eric Kimmel
illustrated by Carolyn Croll

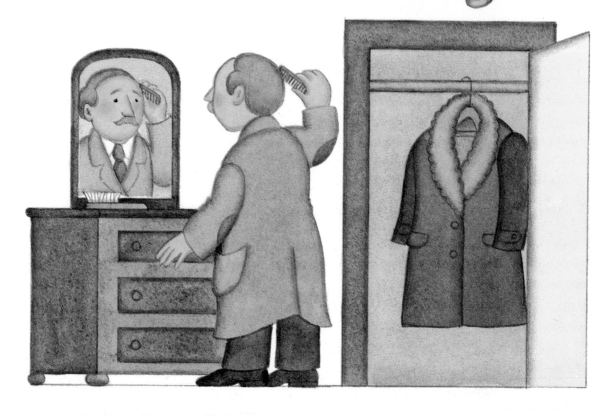

Paul combed his hair. He put on his old coat. He had a fine new coat, but he loved the old one. His own cousin Walter had invited him to a ball. Walter was very rich and Paul was very poor, but they were friends. Paul always had a good story to tell.

Paul walked fast because he wanted to get there early. "Then I'll be able to eat all I want," he thought.

Paul walked to the gate in the wall. He knocked on Walter's door. A tall man came to the door. But he would not let Paul in! He thought Paul was not invited.

"Go away!" said the man. "You can't be a friend of Walter's. All of Walter's friends wear fine clothes."

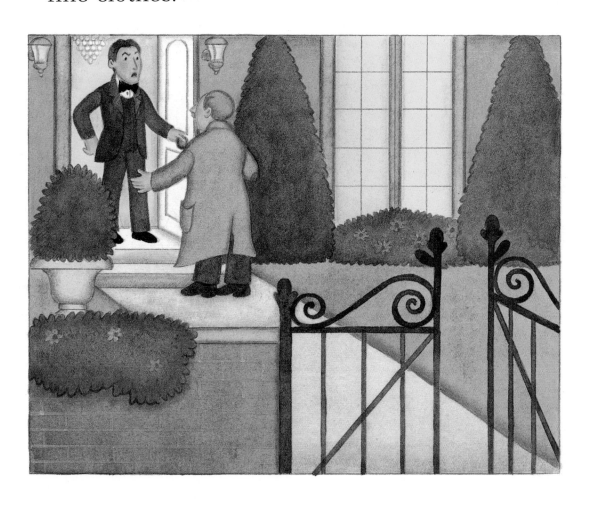

"But I am Walter's cousin!" Paul cried. "Talk to him! He knows who I am!"

The man shut the door.

Paul walked down the street. "I know what to do," thought Paul. He went home and put on his other coat. Then he walked back to Walter's house.

The same tall man came to the door. He looked at Paul's fine coat. He let him into the hall.

At the ball, Paul saw a table filled with good things to eat. He knew what he would do. He went to the plates and saucers on the table. He put some lamb meat into one pocket of his coat. He put cake into the other pocket. He was able to fill all the pockets of the coat with food.

"Paul, welcome to the ball! But what are you doing?" Walter asked. "Why aren't you eating? Why are you putting all the food into your coat? It looks as if the coat were eating, not you."

"I have a story to tell you, Walter," said Paul. "I came to your house, but I was not welcome because I wore my old coat. So I went home and put on another coat. When I came back wearing this fine coat, I was welcome."

Paul went on. "When you invited me to the ball, I thought you wanted me to come. I was wrong. You wanted someone in a fine coat. You really invited the coat. So I say let the coat eat!"

Walter thought a bit. He said, "I am sorry. You are my friend, not the coat. Come. Sit, eat, talk. Tell me and my friends another story. After all, a coat might eat, but it can't tell a good story."

The Rooster
Who Went to His Uncle's Wedding

A LATIN AMERICAN FOLKTALE

retold by Alma Flor Ada
illustrated by Kathleen Kuchera

Early one morning, when the sun had not yet appeared, the rooster of this story was busy shining his beak and combing up his feathers. It was the day of his uncle's wedding, and the rooster wanted to be on time.

When everything looked perfect he set off down the road with a brisk and springy walk. With each step the rooster nodded his head, thinking of all the wonderful things waiting for him at the wedding banquet.

Before long his stomach began to growl.
"I wish I'd eaten breakfast," he said. Then
something caught his eye. There, next to the
road, sat a single golden kernel of corn.

Perfect, the rooster thought. But when he got
closer he could see that the kernel was lying in
a puddle of mud. If he ate it he would get his
beak all dirty.

Oh, that rooster was hungry. But he couldn't
go to his uncle's wedding with a dirty beak.
What to do? Peck or not peck? he wondered.

The rooster stared at the kernel.

Then with one sharp peck he gobbled it down
. . . and wound up with a beak full of mud.

So the rooster looked around quickly for someone who could help him. First he noticed the grass growing on the side of the road.

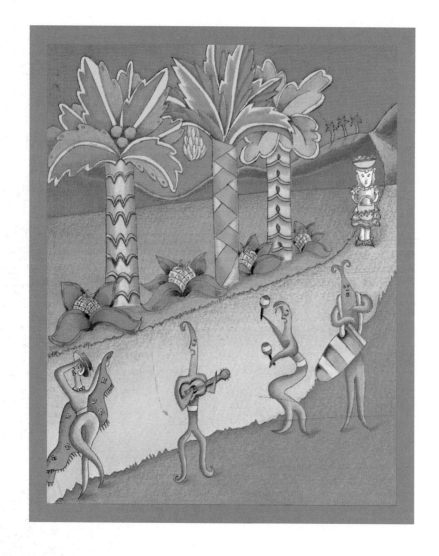

The rooster said to the grass:
"Dear grass, velvety grass,
won't you please clean my beak
so that I can go to my own uncle's wedding?"
But the grass answered:
"No, I won't. Why should I?"

The rooster looked around to see if there was anyone else who could help him. Just then he saw a lamb grazing in the field. Maybe he could *scare* the grass into helping. So he asked the lamb:

"Dear lamb, woolly lamb,
please eat the grass
that won't clean my beak
so that I can go to my own uncle's wedding."
But the lamb answered:
"No, I won't. Why should I?"

But the grass cried out very loudly:

"No, please don't eat me. I will clean the rooster's beak."

And before you know it the rooster's beak shone as bright as the day.

So the rooster said good-bye to everyone with a happy "Cock-a-doodle-doo!" and went on his way to his uncle's wedding. And he walked with a brisk and springy walk, to get there on time for the banquet.

About the Author
Alma Flor Ada

Alma Flor Ada grew up in a family of storytellers. Her grandmother, father, and uncle told her many tales. "It is not a surprise that I like to tell stories," says Ms. Ada. Ms. Ada's grandmother told her the story of "The Rooster Who Went to His Uncle's Wedding."

Reader Response

Let's Talk
Have you ever needed help from someone else? Tell about it.

Let's Think
What happens when the sun agrees to help? Why?

Test Prep
Let's Write
Pretend that the sun did not help the rooster. Write a new ending for the story.

Make a Story Map

Draw a picture that shows the characters, setting, problem, and solution of the story.

1. Fold a sheet of paper into four parts.
2. Write one of these headings on each part.

Character   Setting   Problem   Solution

3. Draw pictures for each part.
4. Retell the story to others. Use the story map.

Language Arts

Adjectives with -er and -est

Use adjectives when you compare nouns.
Add **-er** to an adjective when you compare
two nouns. Add **-est** when you compare
more than two nouns.

The blue present is **big.**
The red present is **bigger** than the
blue present.
The yellow present is the **biggest** of all.

Talk

Talk about the picture. What
is big, short, or tall? Add **-er**
or **-est** to compare two or
more nouns.

Write

Write these sentences. Choose an adjective with **-er** or **-est**.

1. The____ candle is blue.
   (smaller, smallest)
2. The pig is____ than the mouse.
   (bigger, biggest)

Write sentences of your own. Use an adjective to compare three people, places, or things. Remember to add **-er** or **-est.** Draw a picture to go with your sentences.

Yawning Dawn

by Helen Lester

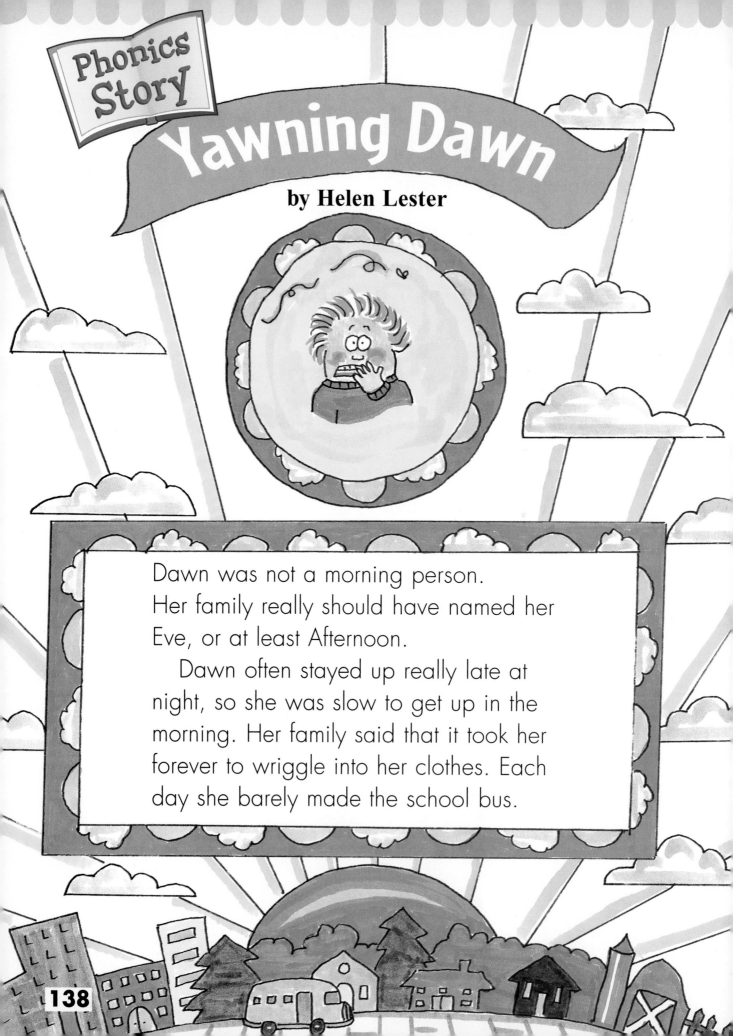

Dawn was not a morning person. Her family really should have named her Eve, or at least Afternoon.

Dawn often stayed up really late at night, so she was slow to get up in the morning. Her family said that it took her forever to wriggle into her clothes. Each day she barely made the school bus.

On Saturday, Janine
and Coco did everything
together.

153

On Sunday, the family went to the mall. Coco came too.

They went from store to store, searching for just the right shoes. Finally they each found the perfect pair, along with lots of other things.

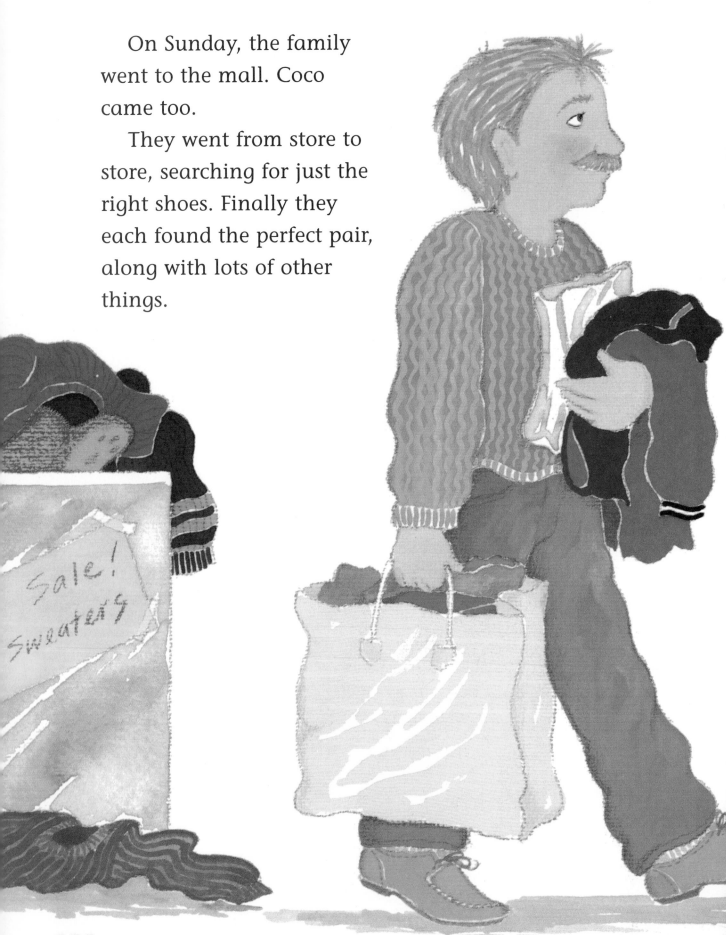

"I'm starving," said Mom. "Let's go for lunch."

They piled their bags into the booth.

"Let's get a highchair for Coco," said Janine.
". . . Coco . . . WHERE'S COCO?"

They looked in all the bags. No Coco. Dad
looked under the table. No Coco.

"OH, NO!" cried Janine. "I LOST COCO!"

"Calm down," said Dad. "We'll just retrace our steps."

"Dad, we were in every store in this mall," moaned Janine. "We'll never find him!"

The family spent the rest of the afternoon searching the mall for Coco.

They even checked the Lost and Found Department three times.

On Monday morning, Janine had to go to school without Coco. She stood in front of the class and read from his diary:

Weekend:

I went home with Janine on Friday. On Saturday we rode her bike. On Sunday I got lost in the mall!

Please help Janine find me!

A tear rolled down Janine's cheek.

"Don't worry, Janine—we'll all help," said
Mrs. Robin.

"How about if we make posters?" suggested Addie.

"Great idea." Mrs. Robin handed out paper.

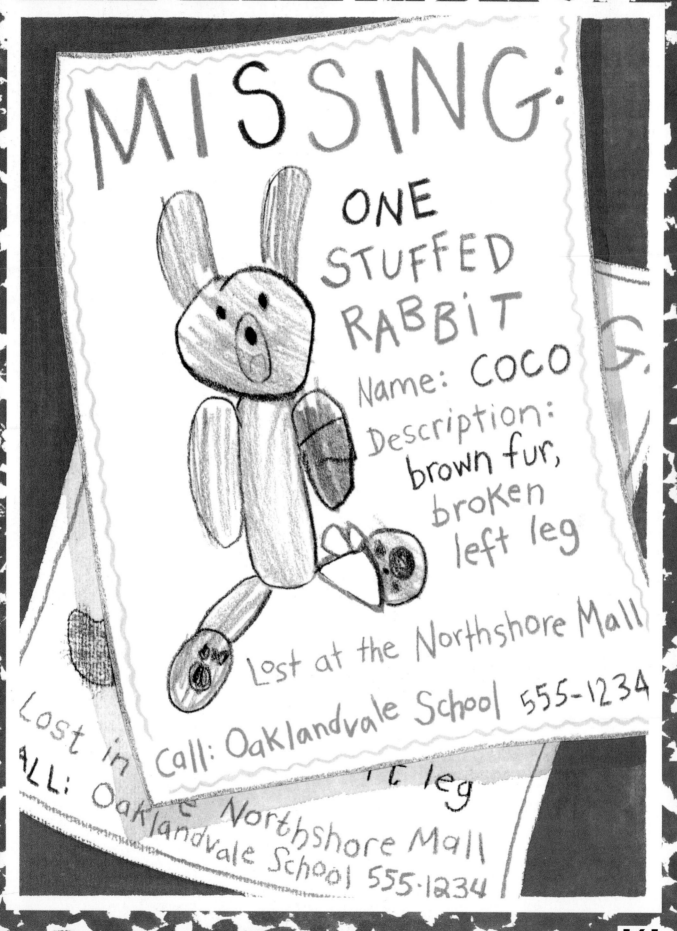

On Tuesday after school, Mrs. Robin, Janine, and three classmates went to the mall. They hung up all the posters and checked the Lost and Found Department again. No Coco.

As they were leaving, Addie noticed a display. The sign read: "TOY DRIVE. New or good used toys wanted."

Addie and Janine ran to the counter.

"Where do all these toys go?" asked Janine.

"We bring them to the Children's Hospital," said the woman.

"Mrs. Robin!" called Janine. "I'll bet Coco is at the hospital!"

"Let's go!" shouted the children.

They all rushed to the hospital.
As they ran inside, they saw something
amazing. A big green frog was handing
out toys. And poking out of the top of
his basket was one stuffed rabbit—*Coco!*

Just then the frog gave Coco to a
little girl.

"Thank you," said the little girl.
"Look, he has a broken leg just like me!"

"Uh-oh," whispered Janine.

"Isn't he cute?" The little girl held up Coco. "I'm going to name him Cinnamon. I'm going to take care of him."

She gave Coco a big hug. "Cinnamon really needs me."

Janine looked at her friends, then at her teacher.

She cleared her throat.

"I think Coco—I mean, Cinnamon—was lucky to find you."

Janine moved closer to the little girl. "My name is Janine."

"I'm Teresa."

At that moment the frog gathered everyone together for some photos. *SNAP. SNAP.* He gave pictures to Janine and Teresa.

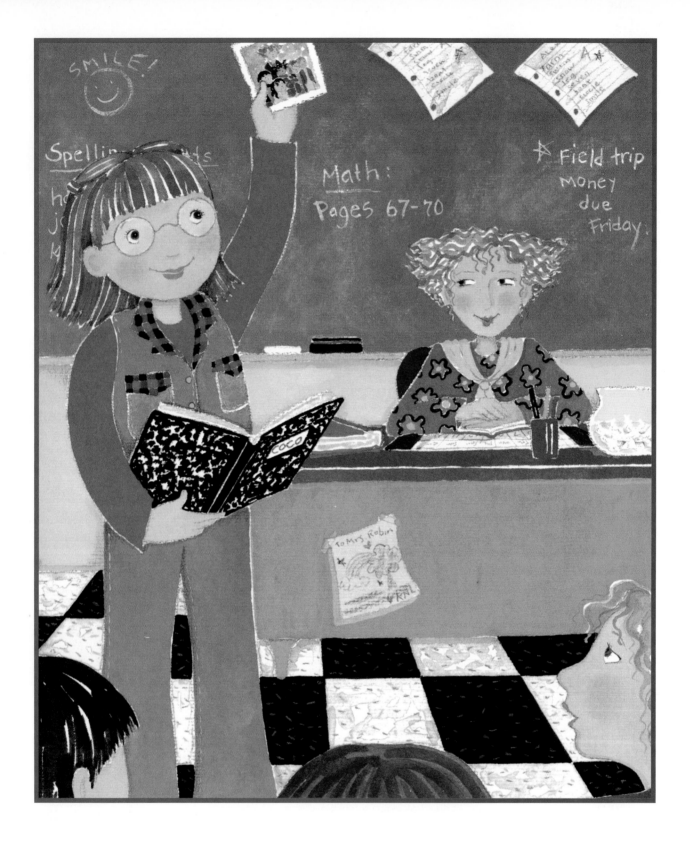

The next morning, Janine stood in front of
the class and held up the picture. She read from
Coco's diary.

Tuesday:
    Janine and the others found me. I am now with someone who really needs me. Her name is Teresa. She loves me and will take good care of me. I had a lot of fun in your class, but I won't be coming back.
          Love,
          Coco

P.S. My new name is
      Cinnamon.
P.P.S. Please write to
      Teresa and me.

And that's just what they did.

My spaceship will travel around Earth. It will have a big table in the middle of it. Astronauts from all different countries will eat together.

Every night we will all cook a dish from another country. After dinner, we will talk for a long time. At the touch of a button, everything will be cleaned up. It will be no trouble at all.

Here are some of the things on my spaceship:
1. Books from different countries
2. Enough games for everyone to play
3. Windows everywhere

People will have enough time to read and play games. They will become friends.

From the spaceship they will look out the windows. They will see the beautiful blue and green Earth. They will remember that we all share this planet together.

Man on the Moon

by Anastasia Suen
illustrated by Benrei Huang

● ● ● ● ● ● ● ● ● ● ●

Moon,
do you remember
your first visitors?

It was 1969 . . .
Astronauts Collins, Aldrin,
and Armstrong suited up.

Each had flown in space, but no one had
ever touched the moon.
No one.

Some said it couldn't be done. Astronauts Collins,
Aldrin, and Armstrong were going to try.

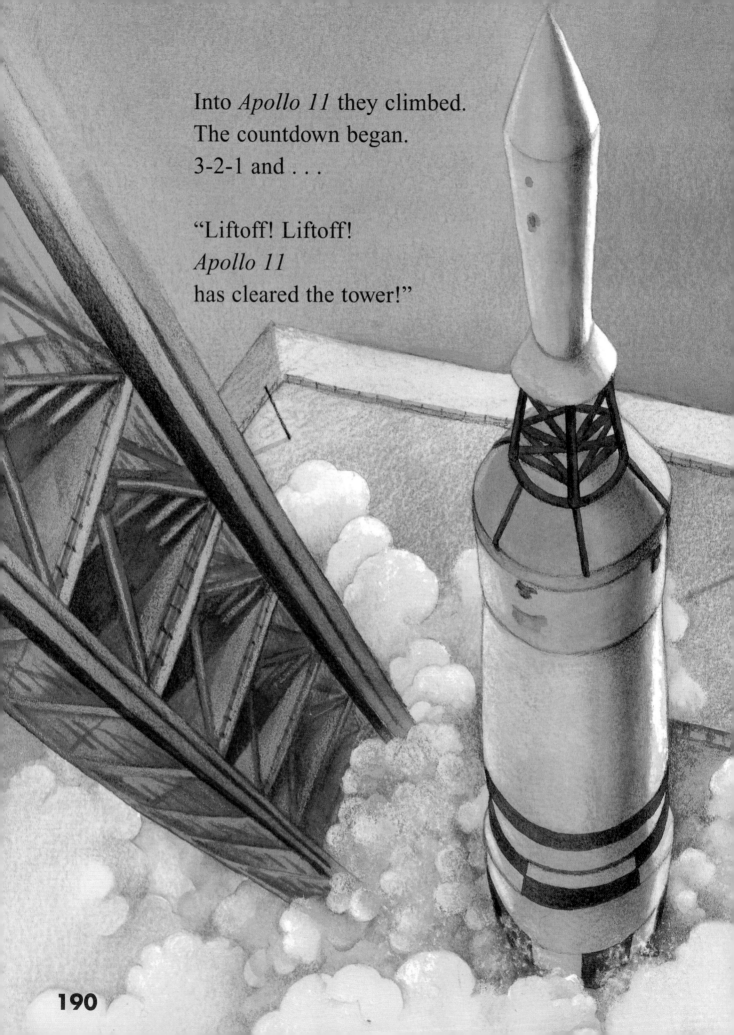

Into *Apollo 11* they climbed.
The countdown began.
3-2-1 and . . .

"Liftoff! Liftoff!
Apollo 11
has cleared the tower!"

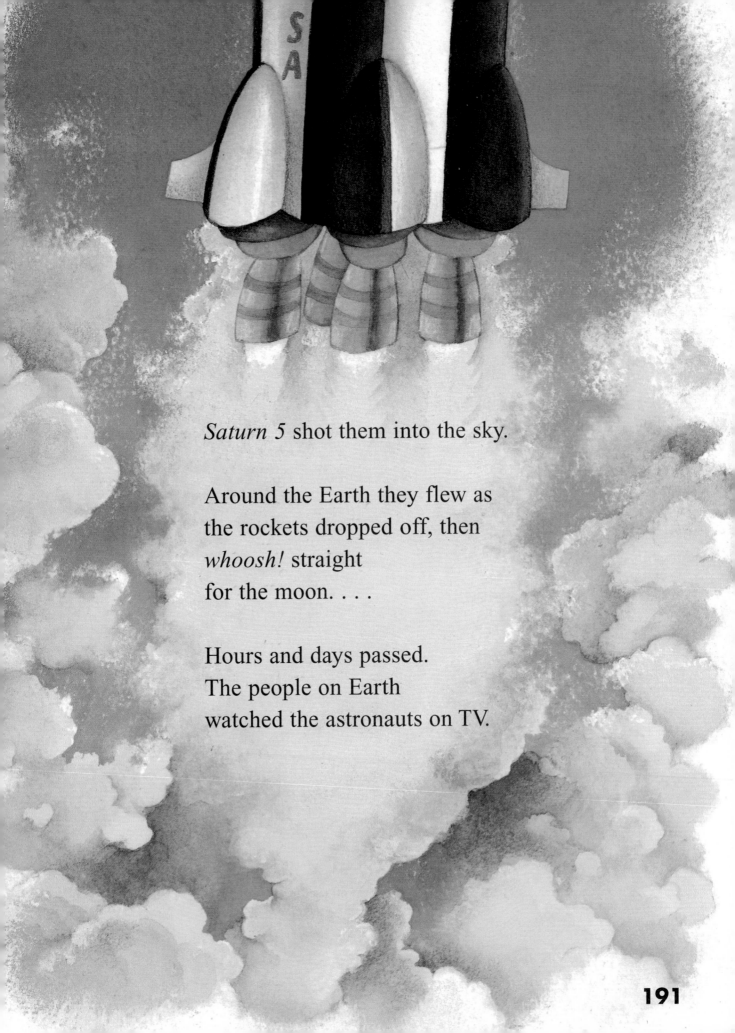

Saturn 5 shot them into the sky.

Around the Earth they flew as
the rockets dropped off, then
whoosh! straight
for the moon. . . .

Hours and days passed.
The people on Earth
watched the astronauts on TV.

Over and over the capsule turned.

Suddenly, the sky went dark.

It was the moon!
For the first time,
Apollo 11 saw the moon.

The astronauts circled, looking for a place to land.
In the morning, their spacecraft would separate.

Columbia, named after Columbus,
would sail around the moon.
The *Eagle,* like a bird, would fly there.

The next day,
Aldrin and Armstrong
climbed into the *Eagle*.

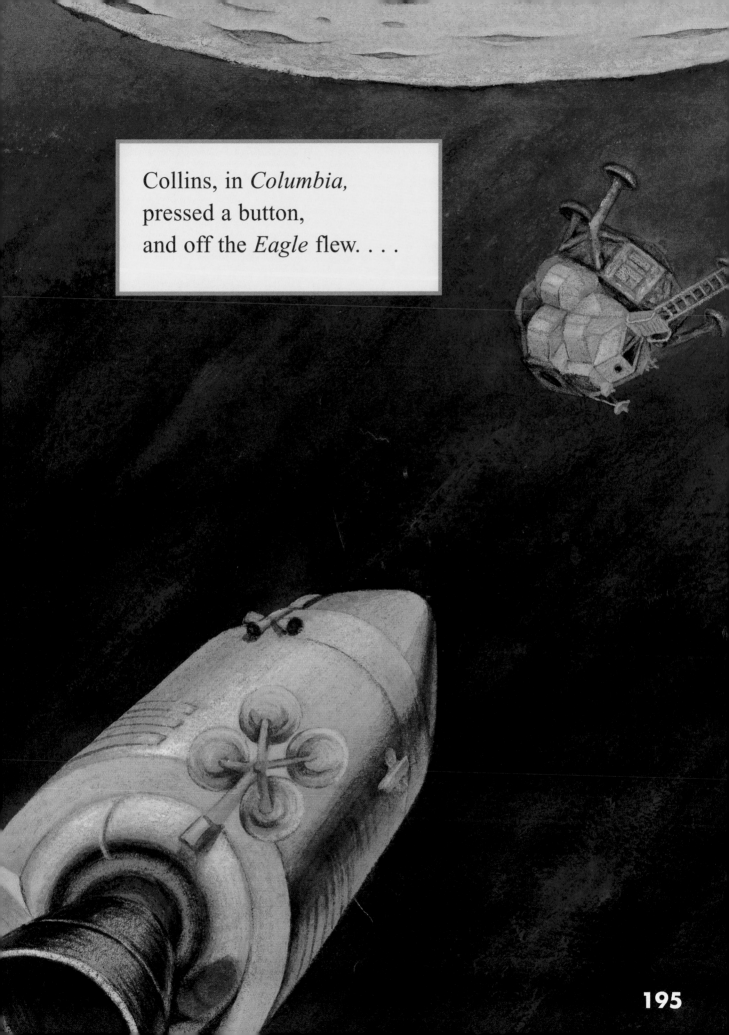

Collins, in *Columbia,*
pressed a button,
and off the *Eagle* flew. . . .

Buttons and gadgets,
switches and lights!
Alarms rang again and again.

In the control room, Houston said, "Go."
The *Eagle* flew on.

On the moon,
craters loomed.
The *Eagle* was going too fast!

Armstrong took the controls
and began to fly.
Houston and the Earth waited.

Fifty feet . . . thirty feet . . .
Contact!

"Houston,
Tranquility Base here.
The *Eagle* has landed."

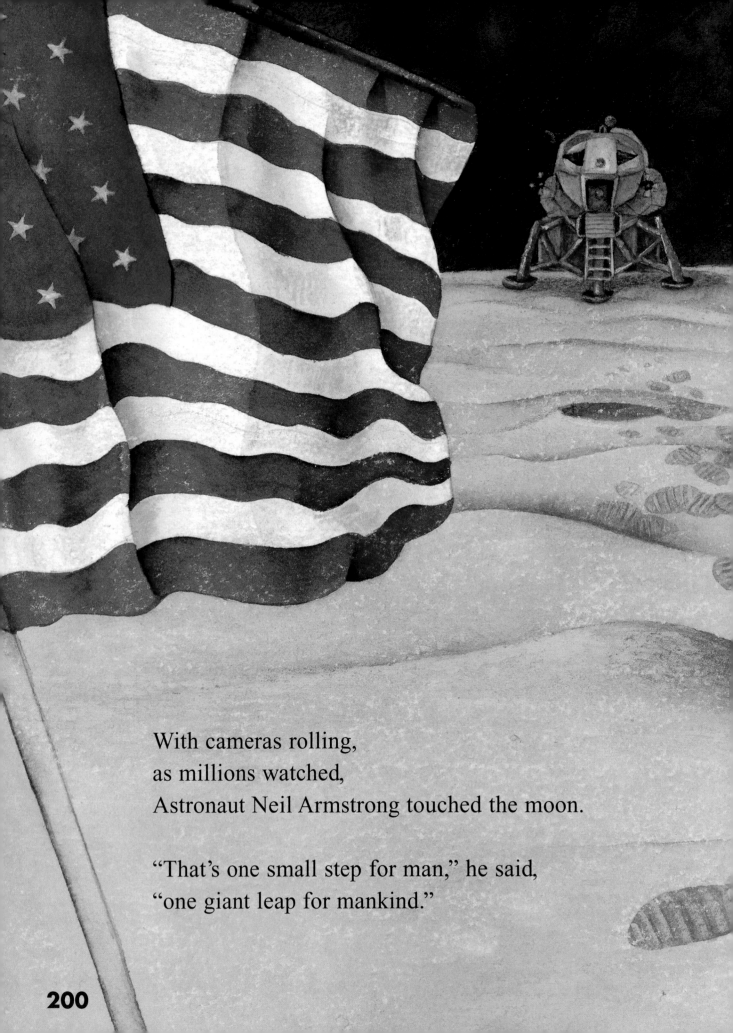

With cameras rolling,
as millions watched,
Astronaut Neil Armstrong touched the moon.

"That's one small step for man," he said,
"one giant leap for mankind."

Aldrin and Armstrong
took pictures, collected rocks,
and planted the American flag.

Hours later,
the *Eagle* left the moon
and linked up with *Columbia*.

Home again,
Collins, Aldrin, and Armstrong
splashed down in the Pacific Ocean.

Some said it couldn't be done.
Mike Collins, Buzz Aldrin, and
Neil Armstrong proved them
wrong . . .

and made history.

Glossary

Words from *Man on the Moon*

astronaut

astronaut
> a person who rides in a spacecraft

capsule
> the front part of a rocket

controls
> buttons and other tools for operating a spacecraft

countdown
> the calling out of the seconds left before a spacecraft lifts off

crater

crater
> a hole in the ground that is shaped like a bowl

gadget
> a small tool

liftoff
> the raising into the air of a rocket or spacecraft

liftoff

spacecraft
> something astronauts ride in to travel in space

About the Author

Anastasia Suen

When Anastasia Suen was a child, her family lived in Florida. "I grew up with NASA" (the National Aeronautics and Space Administration, which directs the U.S. space program), says Ms. Suen. She and her brother watched from their backyard as rockets took off into space. She watched the *Eagle*'s moon landing on TV with her family.

Reader Response

Let's Talk

If you were going to the moon, what part of the trip would you look most forward to?

Let's Think

The author says, "Some said it couldn't be done." What does she mean?

Test Prep
Let's Write

Pretend you are an astronaut on the moon. Send a postcard to your family and friends. Write about your trip.

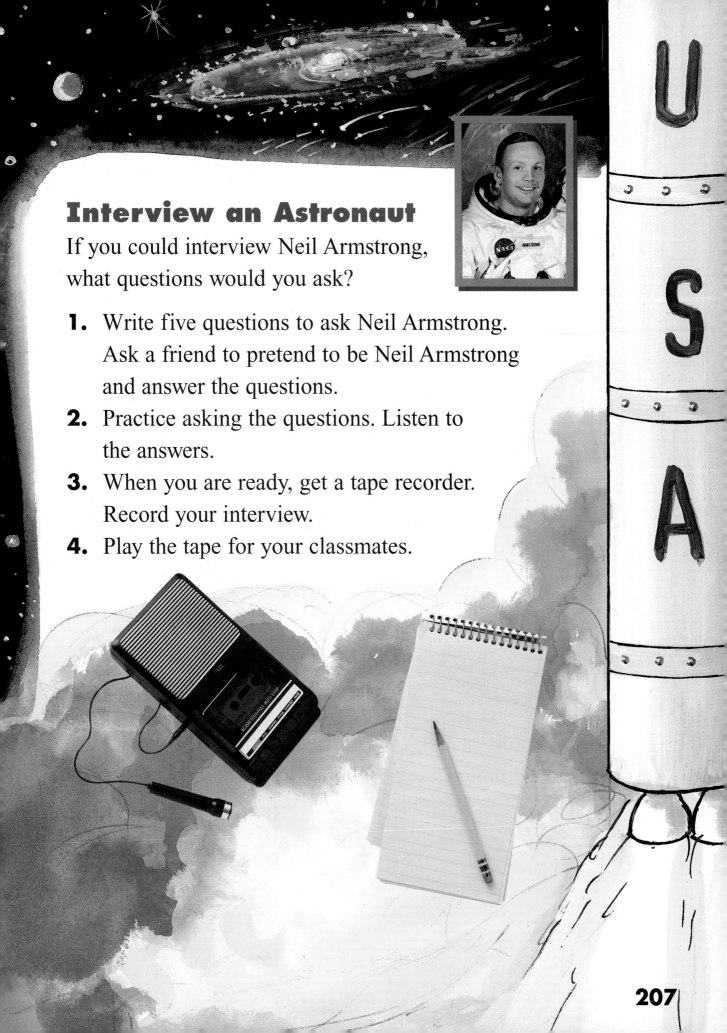

Interview an Astronaut

If you could interview Neil Armstrong, what questions would you ask?

1. Write five questions to ask Neil Armstrong. Ask a friend to pretend to be Neil Armstrong and answer the questions.

2. Practice asking the questions. Listen to the answers.

3. When you are ready, get a tape recorder. Record your interview.

4. Play the tape for your classmates.

Language Arts

Pronouns

A **pronoun** is a word that takes the place of a noun or nouns. **I, he, she, it, we,** and **they** are pronouns.

The boy dreams in his bedroom.
He dreams in his bedroom.

The rocket takes off.
It takes off.

The astronauts land on the moon.
They land on the moon.

Use the pronoun **I** in place of your name.

I love space!

Talk

Find people, places, or things in the picture. Name the noun. Tell what pronoun to use in place of each noun.

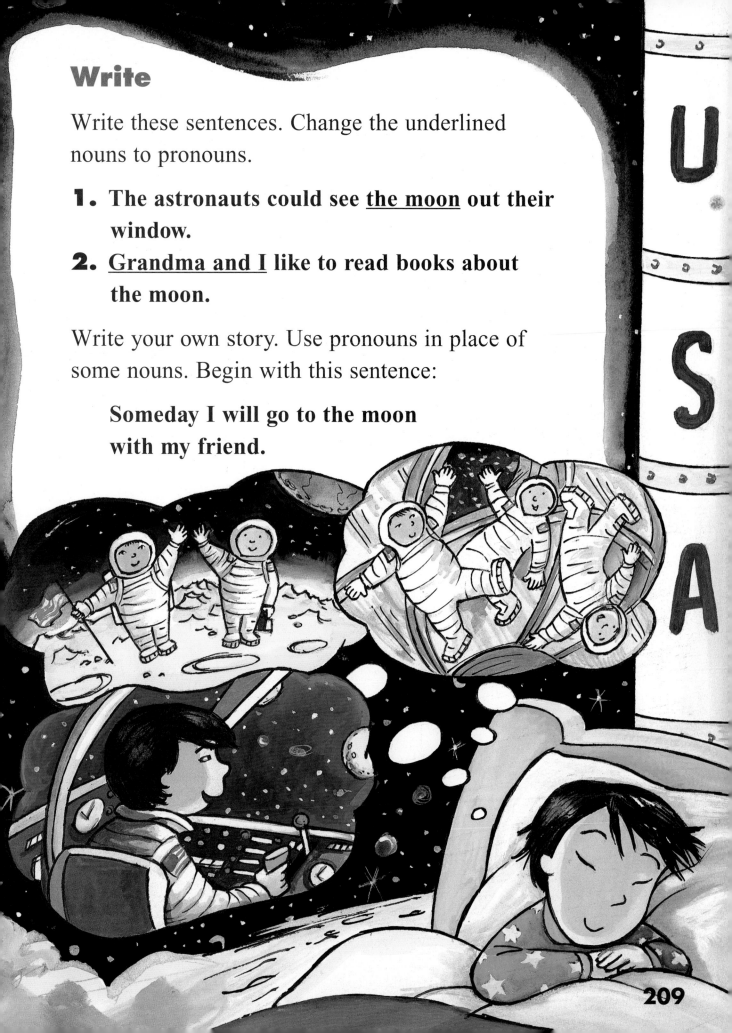

Write

Write these sentences. Change the underlined nouns to pronouns.

1. The astronauts could see **the moon** out their window.
2. **Grandma and I** like to read books about the moon.

Write your own story. Use pronouns in place of some nouns. Begin with this sentence:

Someday I will go to the moon with my friend.

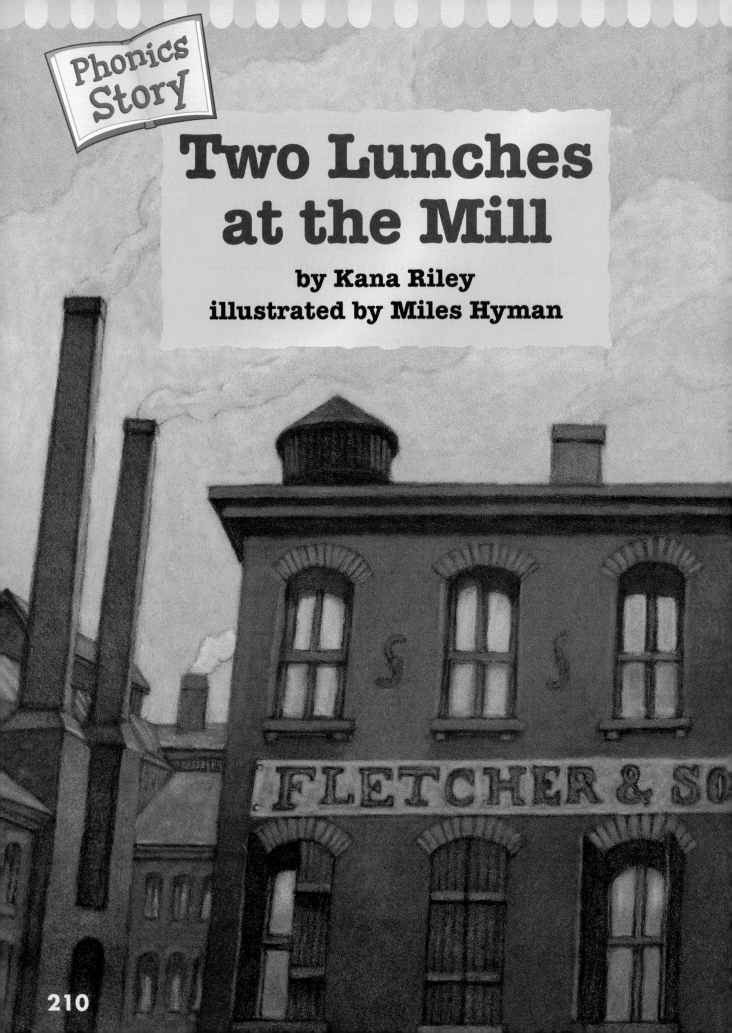

Two Lunches
at the Mill

by Kana Riley

illustrated by Miles Hyman

FLETCHER & SO

Bong! Bong! Above us, the bell in the mill tower begins to ring. "Lunch time!" says my grandma. I call her Gran.

Gran's humble family once worked in the cloth mill.

"The bell in the tower was our family clock," Gran says. "At noon, when the bell rang, we knew it was time to eat. Mama would pack lunches for everyone.

"My sister Jenny would walk across the
street to the mill with the lunch boxes.
People from all the houses did the same
thing. One day I went along with Jenny.
She carried boxes of sandwiches for our big
sisters. I carried only one. It was for Papa.
I walked along behind Jenny.

"She opened the door to a big room. There stood row upon row of machines. People sat only inches apart upon simple, maple benches. What a rumble of noises! There were clashes and hisses all around.

"Jenny ran ahead. I looked around. I called for her. But no one could hear a word I said.

"So I scrambled out the door . . . right into Papa!

" 'You brought sandwiches,' he said. 'And peaches . . . and an apple! You sure are a good girl!'

"After that, I carried his lunch every day," says Gran. "Soon I knew my way around all the places in the mill."

Gran looks at the dresses in the shop windows as we walk. "Upon my word," she says, "what pretty red sashes."

Then she turns to me. "Now, young man, I'm sure you're as hungry as Papa ever was. Let's find a table and order our lunches."

"Sure, Gran," I say.

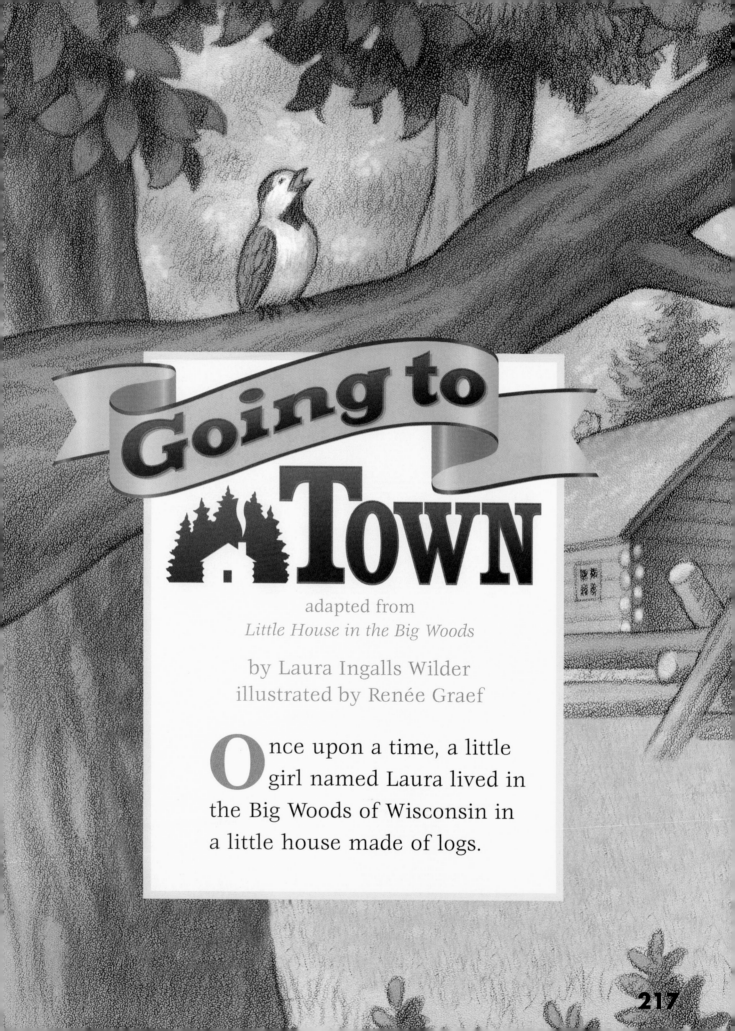

Going to Town

TOWN

adapted from
Little House in the Big Woods

by Laura Ingalls Wilder
illustrated by Renée Graef

Once upon a time, a little girl named Laura lived in the Big Woods of Wisconsin in a little house made of logs.

She lived in the little house with her Pa, her Ma, her big sister Mary, her baby sister Carrie, and their good old bulldog Jack.

One day Pa said that as soon as he had finished planting the crops, they would all go to town. Laura, Mary, and Carrie could go too. They were old enough now.

Laura and Mary were very excited! The next day they tried to play going to town. They could not do it very well, because they were not sure what a town was like. They had never even seen a store.

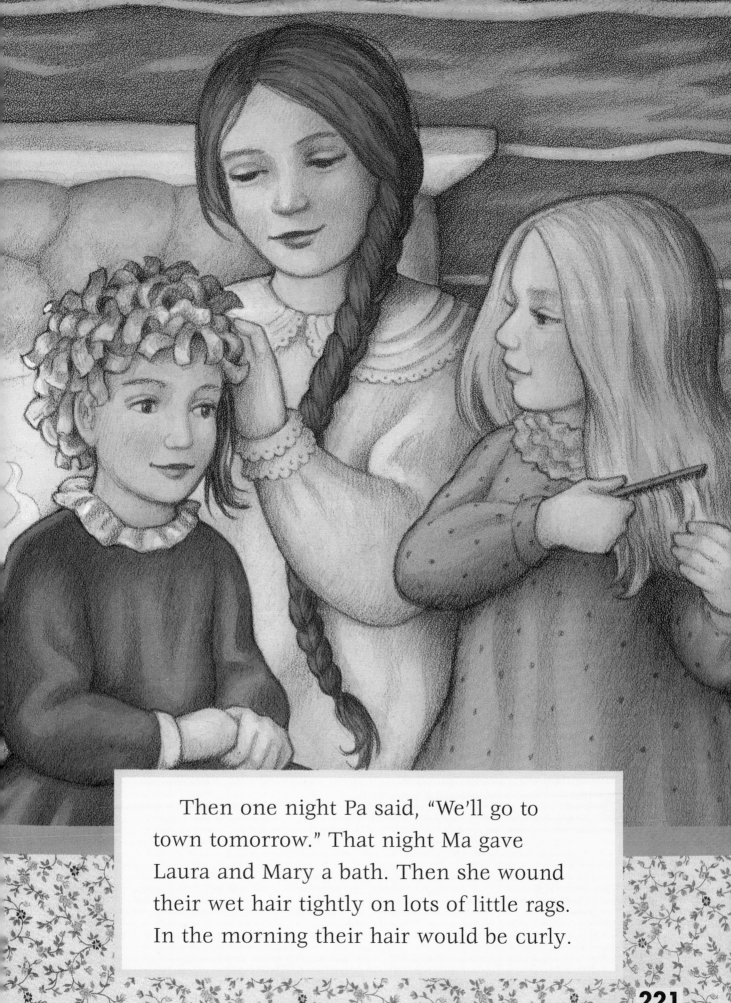

Then one night Pa said, "We'll go to town tomorrow." That night Ma gave Laura and Mary a bath. Then she wound their wet hair tightly on lots of little rags. In the morning their hair would be curly.

When Laura and Mary woke up, they put on their best dresses. Mary buttoned up the back of Laura's red calico dress, and Ma buttoned up the back of Mary's blue calico dress. Then Ma took the rags out of their hair and combed it into long round curls that hung down over their shoulders.

After breakfast Pa drove the wagon up to the gate of the little house. He had brushed the horses until they shone. Ma sat up on the wagon seat with Pa, holding Baby Carrie in her arms. Laura and Mary sat behind Ma and Pa on the board across the wagon box. They were going to town!

They were happy as they rode through the springtime woods. Ma was smiling, Carrie laughed and bounced, and Pa whistled while he drove the horses. Rabbits stood up in the road ahead, and the sun shone through their tall ears. Twice Laura and Mary saw deer looking at them with their large, dark eyes among the trees.

Suddenly Pa stopped the horses and
pointed ahead with his whip. "There you
are, Laura and Mary!" he said. "There's the
town of Pepin."

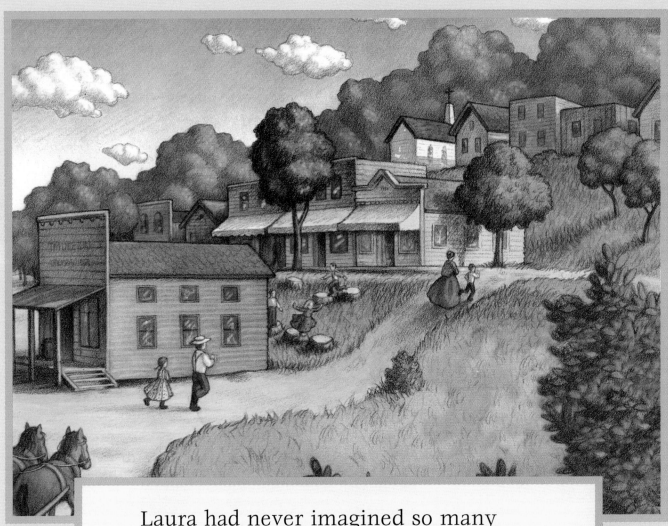

Laura had never imagined so many
houses and so many people. There were
more houses than she could count. Laura
looked and looked, and could not say a word.

Pa helped everyone down from the wagon, and they walked up to the biggest building in town. This was the store where Pa came to trade. As they climbed up the steps of the store, Laura was so excited that she was trembling all over.

The store was full of things to look at. There were sacks of salt and sugar. There were pink and blue and red and brown and purple fabrics for dresses. There were boots and hammers and nails and big wooden pails full of candy. There were so many things that Laura did not know how Pa and Ma could ever choose.

When all the trading was done, the storekeeper gave Mary and Laura each a piece of candy. They were so surprised that they just stood looking at their candies. Then they remembered and said, "Thank you." The candies were shaped like hearts and had printing on them. Mary's candy said:

> *Roses are red,*
> *Violets are blue,*
> *Sugar is sweet,*
> *And so are you.*

Laura's said only:

> *Sweets to the sweet.*

After they left the store, they walked over to the lake at the edge of town. They all sat on the warm sand, and Ma opened the picnic basket that she had brought. Inside there were bread and butter and cheese, hard-boiled eggs, and cookies for lunch.

After the picnic was over, they all got back into the wagon to go home. It was a long trip through the Big Woods to the little house. Laura and Mary were very tired, and Baby Carrie was asleep in Ma's arms. But Pa sang softly:

" 'Mid pleasures and palaces, though
   we may roam,
      Be it ever so humble, there's no place
         like home."

Plan a Trip

Think of places you have been. Where would you like to go? Make a plan for a trip.

1. Think of a place. It can be real or made-up.
2. Answer these questions on a large sheet of paper.
   Where is it?
   What is it called?
   How will you get there?
   What does it look like?
   Where will you stay?
   What can you do there?
3. Draw a picture of the place.
4. Share your plan with a classmate.

237

Language Arts

Singular and Plural Pronouns

A **pronoun** is a word that takes the place of a noun or nouns. Pronouns that tell about one person or thing are **singular.**

The teacher writes on the chalkboard.
She writes on the chalkboard.

Pronouns that tell about more than one person or thing are **plural.**

The students learn to read.
They learn to read.

singular pronouns	plural pronouns
I	we
you	you
he, she, it	they

Talk

Tell how the classroom in the picture is different from your classroom. Use pronouns from the list.

Write

Write these sentences. Change the underlined words to pronouns.

My sister and I like to learn about the past. A long time ago children went to school in log cabins. <u>The children</u> sat on benches. The school was very small. Only a few people could fit in <u>the school</u>. The school had a teacher. <u>The teacher</u> was very strict. <u>My sister and I</u> would like to visit an old school soon.

Pretend that you and your friends are in the old school. Write sentences about it. Use singular and plural pronouns.

A True Boating Family

by David McPhail

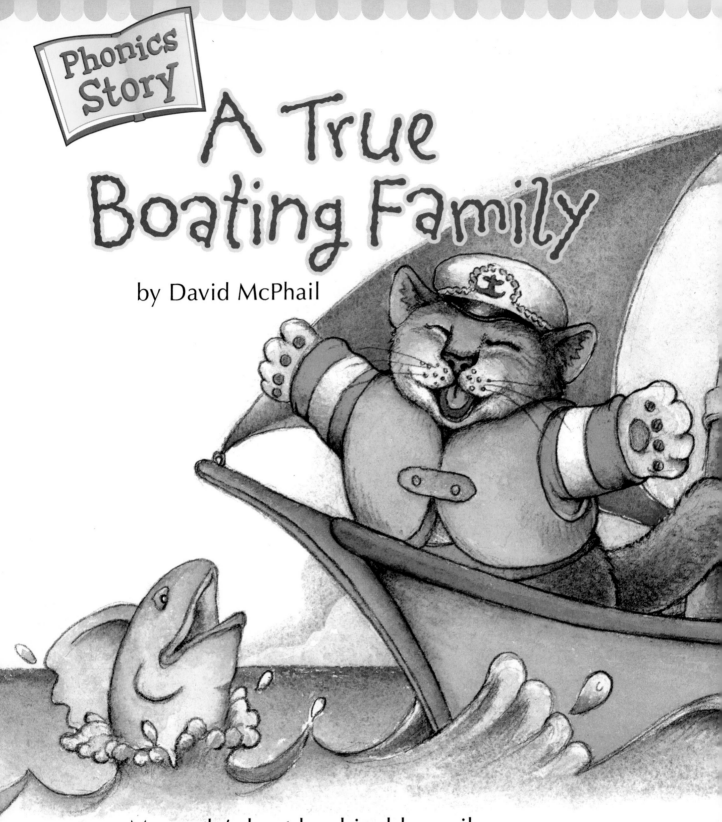

My uncle's boat has big, blue sails.
When he goes by, fish wave their tails.

They jump and seem to sing with him.
My uncle watches as they swim.

My cousin Sue comes on, I hear.
Some days, it's true, she even steers.

My brother has a boat that's small.
He rows it fast, and thrills us all.

He likes to take me. That I know.
He glides through water. See him go!

For years my mother sailed big ships.
She went on many long, long trips.

One ship of hers was called *Sweet Pea.*
It carried things from sea to sea.

Some boxes were red, white, and blue.
They all were full of sticky glue.

My father steers a mighty tug,
which pushes, pulls, and goes
Chug, chug!

He works in every kind of weather.
From time to time, we go together!

Of course, my sister has a boat,
It's tiny, but it sure can float!

Riding the Ferry with Captain Cruz

by Alice K. Flanagan
photographed by Christine Osinski

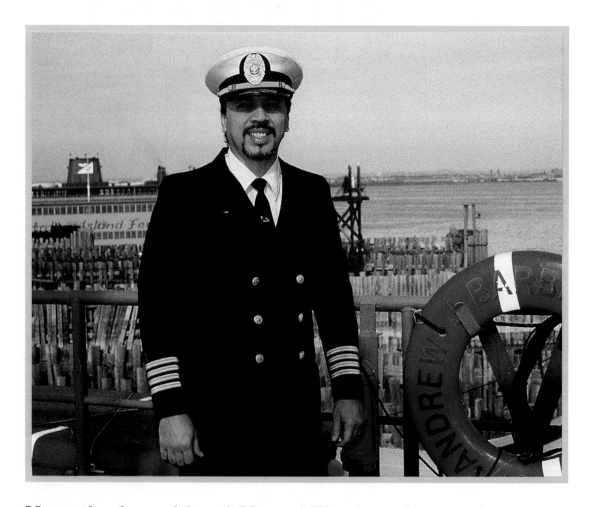

Hear the horn blow? Hurry! The ferryboat is leaving.

See the captain on deck? That's Mr. Cruz, my neighbor.

All day long, Captain Cruz takes people back and forth from Staten Island to New York City, across the bay.

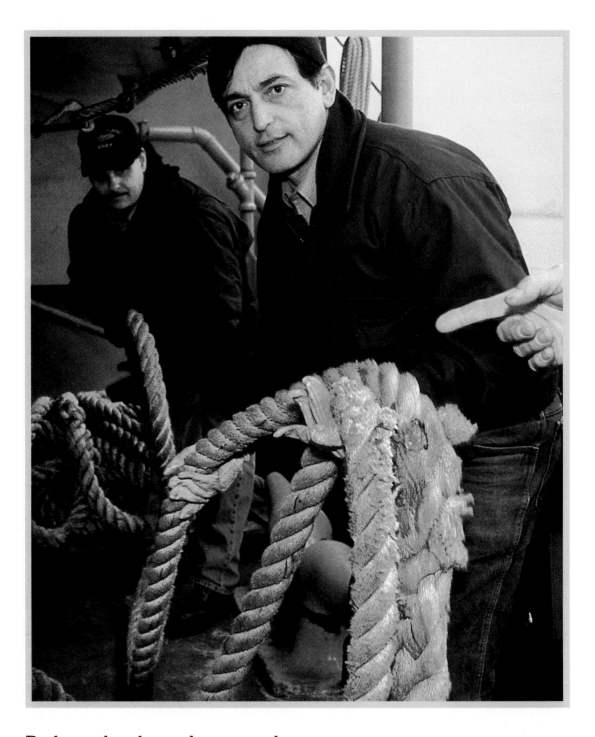

Before the ferry leaves, the crew
makes sure everything on board works.
The trip must be safe!

Hear the engines hum?

Slowly, Captain Cruz steers the ferry away from the dock.

He checks his
compass to see
which direction
the ferry is going.

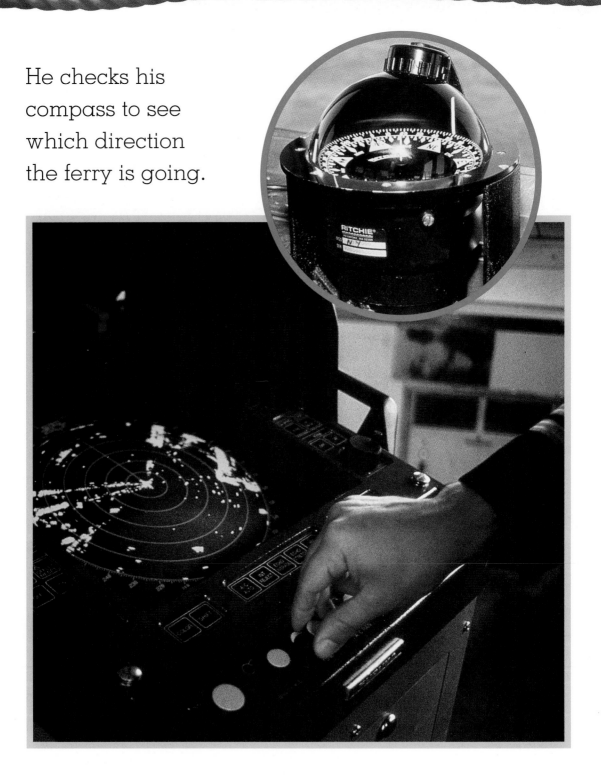

He watches the radar screen. It shows
him how to keep the ferry on course.

Captain Cruz uses a radio to talk with his crew. They are like a family.

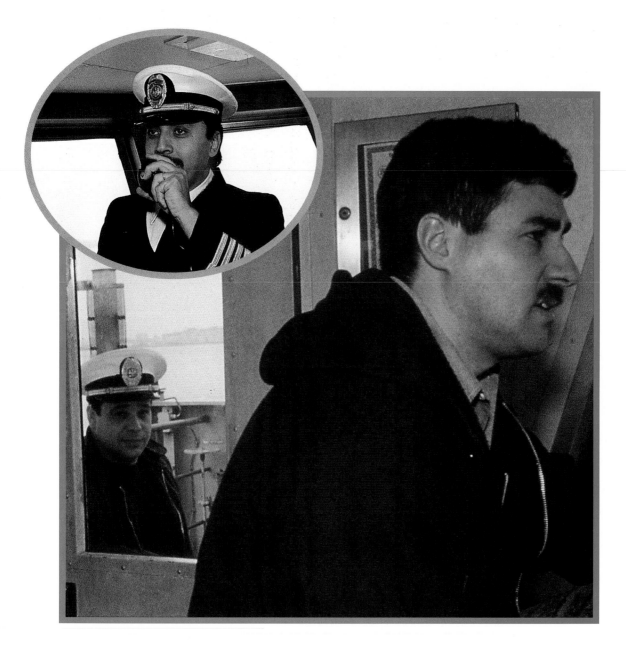

A deckhand sits at the captain's side day and night. He is an extra pair of eyes looking out.

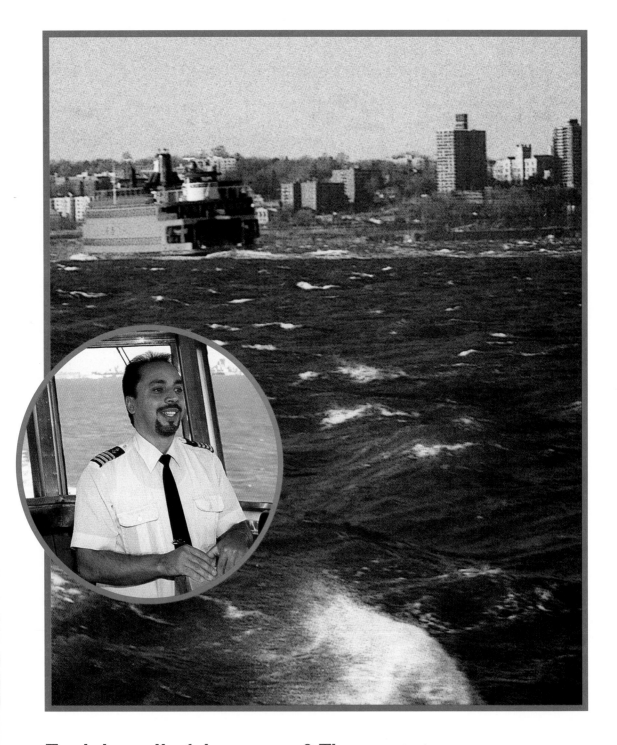

Feel the roll of the waves? The captain handles the ferry well. He has been a ferryboat captain for ten years.

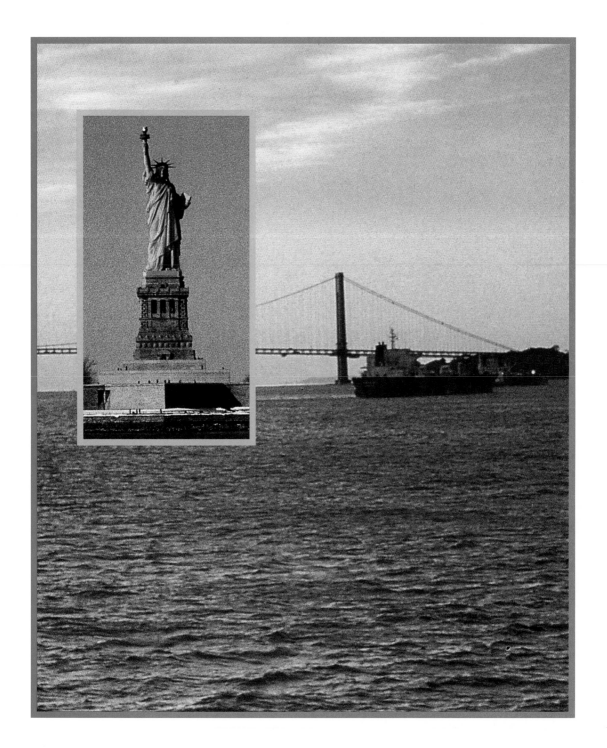

He knows all about the weather and the water
currents, the bridges and the passing ships,
and the famous Statue of Liberty.

Captain Cruz watches these things each
day on his way to and from the city.

Feel the ferry stop?
We have crossed the bay.

After every trip, and at the end of each day,
Captain Cruz writes in the captain's log. He
records what happened along the way.

The captain does his job well.

He helps people get to work safely and on time.

Captain Cruz is careful and responsible. With hard work, he has made his dream of being a ferryboat captain come true!

About the Author

Alice K. Flanagan grew up in Chicago. She loved telling stories. So did her sister Christine Osinski. They also enjoyed drawing pictures together. Now Alice works with her sister to create books for children.

About the Photographer

Christine Osinski takes the photographs that you see in Alice Flanagan's books. Christine lives in Staten Island, New York. That is where Mr. Cruz is a ferryboat captain.

Barcarola

por Nicolás Guillén
illustrado por Shelly Hehenberger

El mar con sus ondas mece
la barca, mece
la barca junto a la costa
brava, la mece
el mar.

Del hondo cielo la noche
cae, la noche
con su gran velo flotando
cae la noche
al mar!

The Boatman's Song

by Nicolás Guillén
illustrated by Shelly Hehenberger

The waves of the sea
rock the boat,
rock the boat by the shore.
The wild sea
rocks the boat.

Out of the deep sky
the night falls,
the night with its floating veil,
the night falls
into the sea.

257

Reader Response

Let's Talk

Would you like to be a ferryboat captain? What would be the best part? What would be the worst part?

Let's Think

Is Captain Cruz a good captain? How do you know?

Test Prep
Let's Write

Pretend you own a ferryboat. You need a captain. Describe the person you would hire for this job.

Act Out Jobs People Do

Captain Cruz dreamed of being a ferryboat captain. What kind of job would you like to have? Act one out.

1. Look through books and magazines. Find a job you would like.
2. Think about people who have that job. What do they do? What special tools, equipment, or clothes do they use?
3. Act out the job for classmates. Can they guess your job?

Language Arts

Pronouns Before and After Verbs

Some pronouns are the subject of the sentence. They come before the verb. These pronouns are **I, he, she, we, they**.

The captain steers the ferry.
He steers the ferry.

Some pronouns come after the verb. These pronouns are **me, him, her, us, them.**

The children wave to **the captain.**
The children wave to **him.**

You can use the pronouns **you** and **it** before or after the verb.

Talk

Make up sentences about the picture. Use nouns. Say the sentences again. Use pronouns. Do they come before or after the verb?

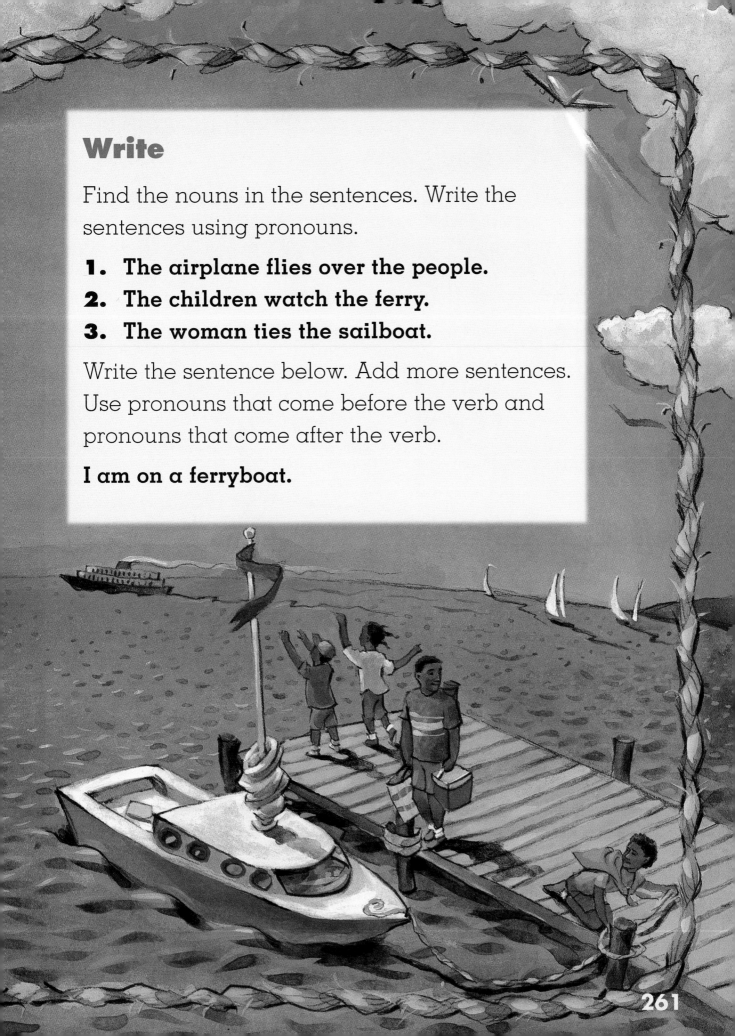

Write

Find the nouns in the sentences. Write the sentences using pronouns.

1. The airplane flies over the people.
2. The children watch the ferry.
3. The woman ties the sailboat.

Write the sentence below. Add more sentences. Use pronouns that come before the verb and pronouns that come after the verb.

I am on a ferryboat.

Splash!

by Susan McCloskey

illustrated by Allan Eitzen

Splash!
Oh, no! Poor Blinkie has fallen into the sea! And the water is terribly cold!

Splash! Splash! Mom and Dad are
diving to the rescue!

Now Blinkie is sinking! Mom and Dad
would grab him, but they can't move any
closer. He's too near that jellyfish.
Jellyfish can sting.

Blinkie is under the sea now.

What is making the water grow dark?
Oh! An octopus is giving off a cloud of
ink. It must be frightened.

The octopus is waving its eight arms.
One arm has reined in Blinkie!

The octopus is swimming away! Mom and Dad scared it off.

Oh, no! Where is Blinkie now?

There's Blinkie! A fish is using its weight to push him away. It's a fish that is fussy about its neighbors.

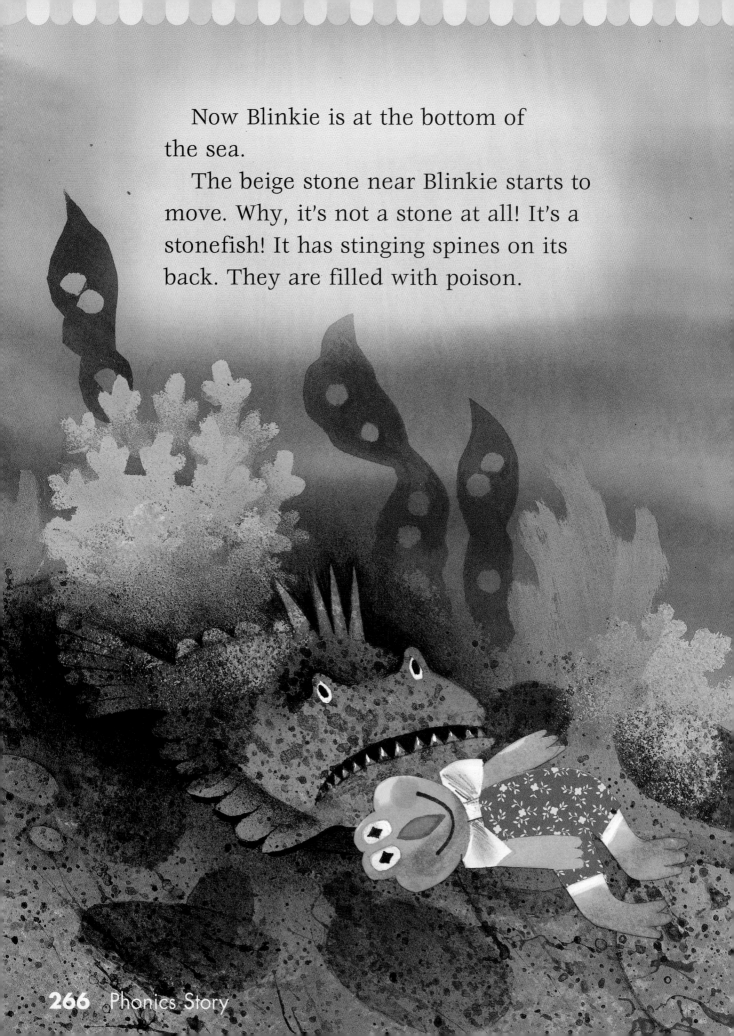

Now Blinkie is at the bottom of the sea.

The beige stone near Blinkie starts to move. Why, it's not a stone at all! It's a stonefish! It has stinging spines on its back. They are filled with poison.

Hooray! Mom and Dad found Blinkie.
Most importantly, they came back safely.
Splash!
Oh, no! Now Dad's camera has fallen
into the sea!

Down in the Sea: The Jellyfish

by Patricia Kite

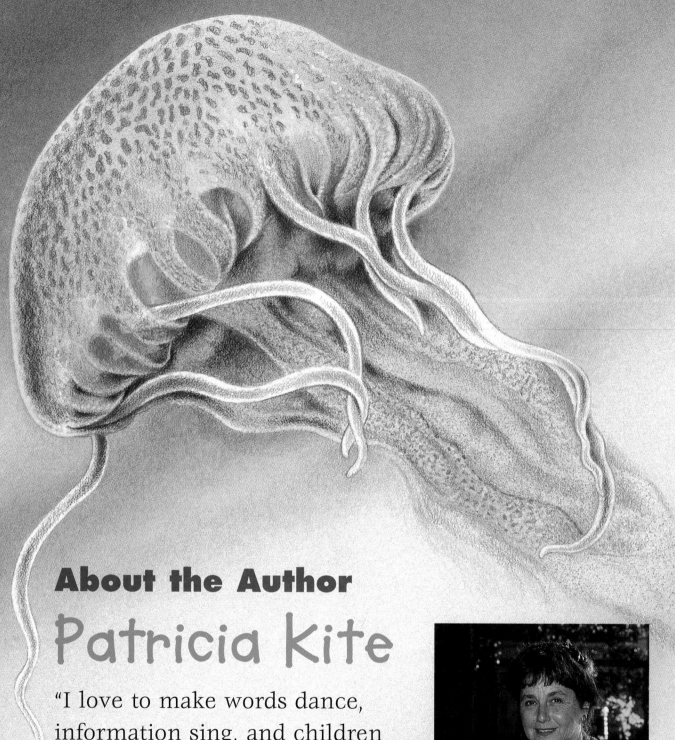

About the Author

Patricia Kite

"I love to make words dance, information sing, and children smile," says Patricia Kite.

Ms. Kite enjoys writing about science. She says she wanted to write about jellyfish because she had always wondered if they "were really made of jelly."

Reader Response

Let's Talk

What facts about the jellyfish surprised you?

Let's Think

What do you think is the most important thing to know about jellyfish? Why?

Test Prep
Let's Write

Pretend you are a jellyfish. Write about a day in your life. Use what you learned to write your story.

Make a Jellyfish

Jellyfish come in many shapes, colors, and sizes. Make your own jellyfish.

1. Draw your jellyfish.
2. Plan what you will need to make the body and the tentacles. Get materials.
3. Make your jellyfish.
4. Hang your jellyfish in the room for classmates to see.

Writing with Pronouns

Pronouns can be the subject of a sentence or come after the verb.

The divers like to look for jellyfish.
They like to look for jellyfish.

The fish saw **the net.**
The fish saw **it.**

When you write, try not to use the same noun over and over again. Use a pronoun to take the place of a noun.

The divers swim deep in the water.
They find fish.

Talk

Tell a story about the picture. Take turns adding sentences. Try not to use the same noun over and over again. Use pronouns in the subject of a sentence or after the verb.

Write

Write these sentences. Find the nouns. Use pronouns in place of some of the nouns.

My family and I went to the ocean last summer. My family and I took a boat out for a day. The boat moved fast. My brothers saw whales and dolphins. My brothers liked the whales and dolphins. My father tried to catch a fish. My father was not very lucky.

Write your own story called **The Best Trip.** Use nouns and pronouns.

Tex and the Big Bad T. Rex

by Mary Blount Christian

illustrated by Bernard Adnet

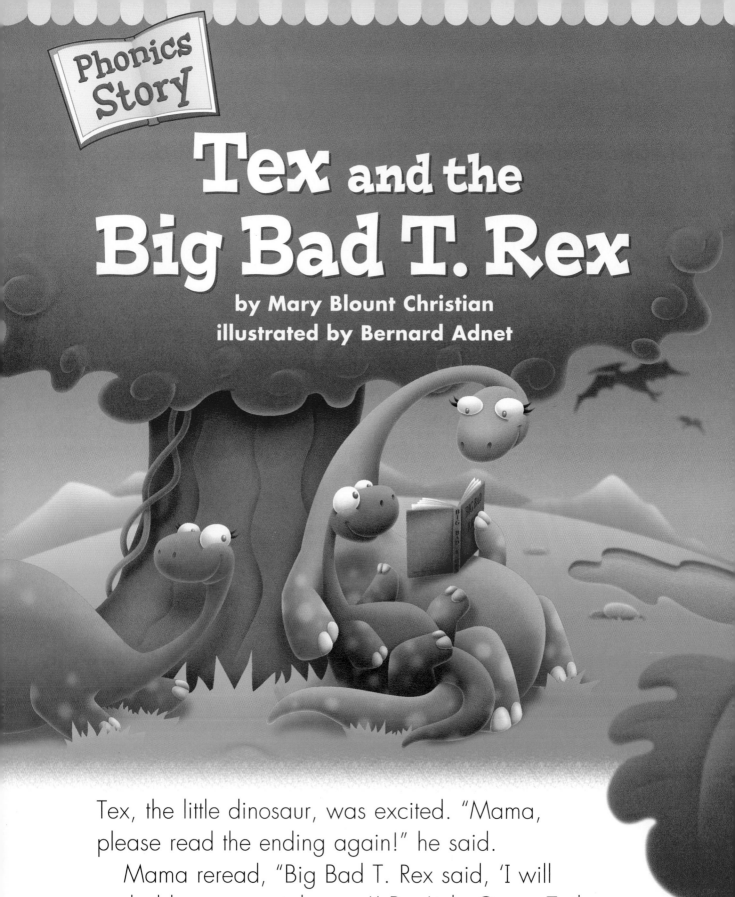

Tex, the little dinosaur, was excited. "Mama, please read the ending again!" he said.

Mama reread, "Big Bad T. Rex said, 'I will probably eat you right now!' But Little Green Tail said, 'Not this day,' and she ran away fast."

Tex said, "If T. Rex comes along someday, I will scare him away like this." He yelled, "Gleep!"

Lexie, his big sister, giggled. "Oh, I am so scared," she teased.

"Be kind to your brother!" Mama exclaimed. "It is unfair to tease him."

Then Mama explained, "You are very brave, Tex, but Big Bad T. Rex goes GRRRONK! It would probably be better for you to run and disappear right away."

GLEEP!

The truth is, it was another sauropod. The tracks look different from the others because these are only the front footprints.

Now wait a minute! Was the sauropod doing some kind of balancing act, walking on its front feet?

What was going on, anyhow?

Here's a clue. Have you ever pushed yourself along in shallow water, "walking" on your hands along the bottom? Your body and feet drift behind you.

That's what the sauropod was doing—pushing itself along in water with its front feet, leaving these "elephant tracks."

Let's go! There are other tracks to follow! Here we are, in a limestone quarry. What's this? Chicken tracks? What's a chicken doing back in dinosaur times?

It does look like chicken tracks. But you're right. There were no chickens in dinosaur times. The tracks were made by a chicken-sized dinosaur named compsognathus.

One hundred forty-five million years ago this 2-foot-long, 6-pound mini-dino ran along on skinny legs and birdlike feet.

What was it doing? It was probably chasing a little lizard, which it ate. The compsognathus is one of the smallest dinosaurs we know of.

Well, this pith helmet is hot.
My canteen is empty. My boots are
covered with mud.

Let's go home and think about the things we've learned from tracking dinosaurs.

"What are you doing?" asked her big brother, Tomás.

"Making a clubhouse," said Rosie.

"It needs a door," said Tomás.

Tomás got some scissors. He cut out a door. Rosie kept painting. She painted a number above the door.

Tomás cut out another piece. It was a window. It looked like half a moon.

"What are you doing?" asked Annie.

"We are making a clubhouse," said Rosie and Tomás.

"It needs curtains," said Annie.

Annie got a piece of cloth. It was big enough to make a curtain. Annie glued it above the window. Then she painted a keyhole.

Rosie painted a doorknob halfway up the door.

Tomás cut out another window.

"What are you doing?" asked Stanley.

"We are making a clubhouse," said Rosie and Tomás and Annie.

"It needs chairs," said Stanley.

Stanley found some boxes. The boxes made good chairs. Rosie painted *CLUBHOUSE* above the window. Annie glued a curtain above another window. Tomás hung a photograph of himself inside.

Soon Rosie's mama heard a sound in the backyard. The sound she heard was laughing.

"What are you doing?" Mama asked.

"We are making a clubhouse," said Rosie and Tomás and Annie and Stanley. "It is big enough for all of us. Money could not buy a better clubhouse!"

"I believe it needs one more thing," said Mama. She got a plate of cookies. They were warm and smelled like honey.

"What a relief! Now our clubhouse is just right," said Rosie and Tomás and Annie and Stanley.

And it was.

Sheri said, "I can make a bar graph. I'll list the number of cups up the side like this. I'll show the days of the week along the bottom like this."

On Monday they set up their corner stand. When people walked by, Petey, Meg's pet parrot, squawked, "Lemonade for sale! Lemonade for sale!"

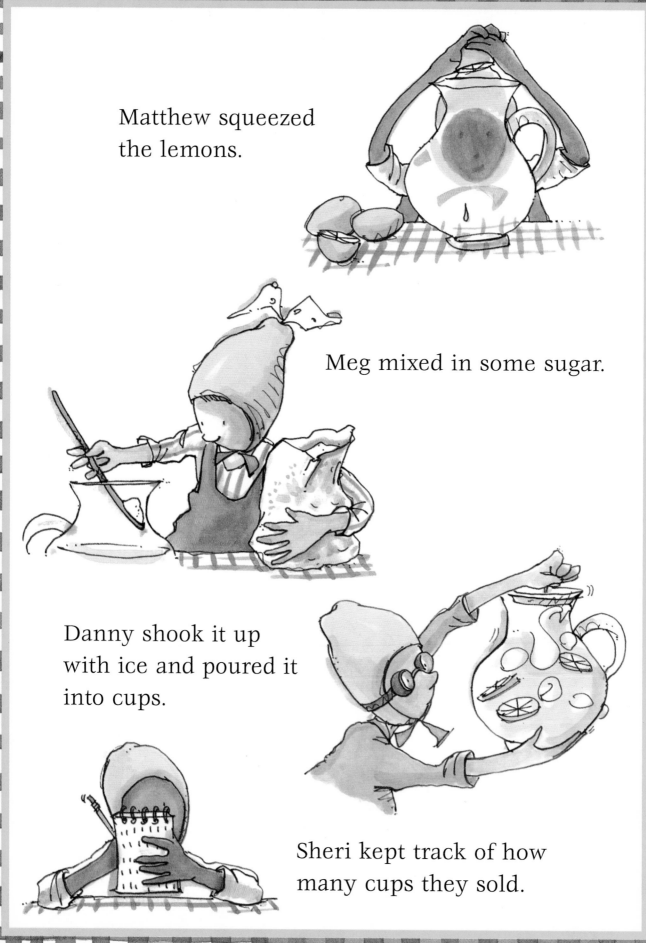

Matthew squeezed the lemons.

Meg mixed in some sugar.

Danny shook it up with ice and poured it into cups.

Sheri kept track of how many cups they sold.

Sheri announced, "We sold 30 cups today. I'll fill in the bar above Monday up to the 30 on the side."

"Not bad," said Danny.

"Not bad. Not bad," chattered Petey.

On Tuesday Petey squawked again,
"Lemonade for sale! Lemonade for sale!"
and more people came by.

Matthew squeezed more lemons.

Meg mixed in more sugar.

Danny shook it up with ice and poured it into more cups.

Sheri kept track of how many cups they sold.

Sheri shouted, "We sold 40 cups today.
I'll fill in the bar above Tuesday up to the
number 40. The bars show that our sales
are going up."

"Things are looking good," said Meg.

"Looking good. Looking good,"
chattered Petey.

On Wednesday Petey squawked,
"Lemonade for sale!" so many times that
most of the neighborhood stopped by.

Matthew squeezed
even more lemons.

Meg mixed in even more sugar.

Danny shook it up with
ice and poured it into
even more cups.

Sheri kept track of how
many cups they sold.

Sheri yelled, "We sold 56 cups today. I'll fill in Wednesday's bar up to a little more than halfway between 50 and 60."

"That's great," shouted Matthew.

"That's great! That's great!" bragged Petey.

On Friday, Sheri arrived with Jed.

"Jed's going to juggle right next to our stand," Sheri said.

That day Petey squawked, Jed juggled, and more people came by than ever before.

Matthew squeezed
loads of lemons.

Meg mixed in
tons of sugar.

Danny shook it up with lots of
ice and almost ran out of cups.

Sheri could hardly keep track
of how many cups they sold.

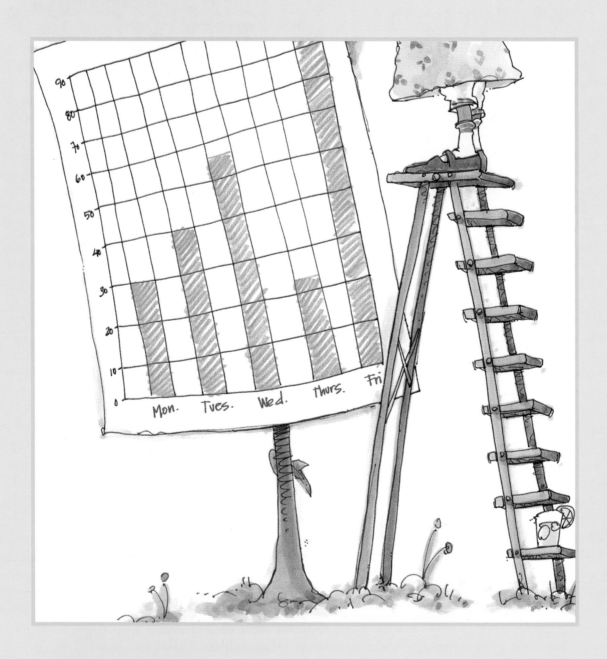

"We sold so many cups today that our sales are over the top. We have enough money to rebuild our clubhouse."

"Hooray!" they all shouted. "Jed! Jed! Will you join our club?"

"You bet!" said Jed.

"You bet! You bet!" squawked Petey.

Bar Graph

If Friday lemonade sales for the Elm Street Kids' Club had gone to the top of the bar graph, how many cups of lemonade would that be? Look at the graph below to see.

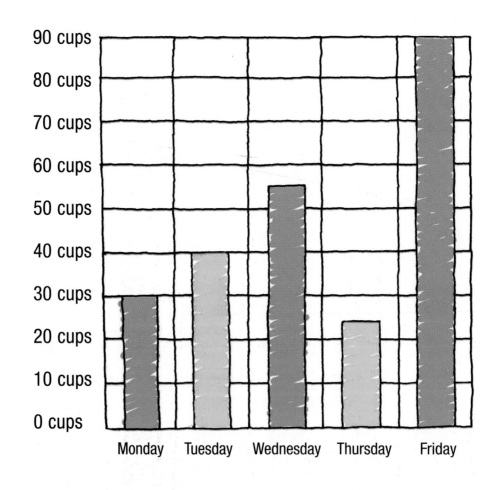

Circle Graph

If Sheri had kept track of the lemonade sales on a circle graph instead of a bar graph, it might have looked like this one.

How many cups of lemonade were sold on Monday?

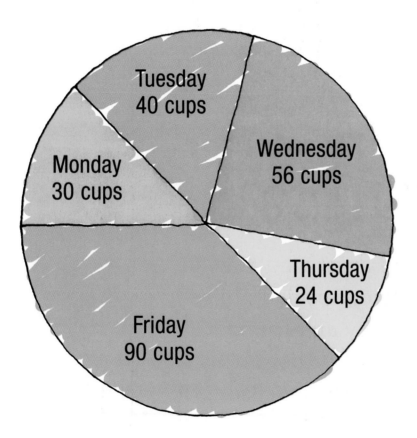

Tuesday
40 cups

Monday
30 cups

Wednesday
56 cups

Thursday
24 cups

Friday
90 cups

About the Author
Stuart J. Murphy

Stuart Murphy lives near Lake Michigan in Illinois. He and his wife enjoy walking along the beach near their home. If they pass a young neighbor selling lemonade along the way, they always buy two cups.

About the Illustrator
Tricia Tusa

Tricia Tusa is an artist who likes to watch people. She especially likes to watch her family and friends. Ms. Tusa gets ideas for her art by looking at their faces. She also looks at their shoes and the way they wear their hair.

Lemonade
for Sale

by John Ciardi

Cut the lemon through the peel.
   The juice is all inside.
When you squeeze it (if it squirts)
   You must step aside.

Lemon squirt can make you smart
   If it hits your eye.
Well, it might not work for you.
   You won't know till you try.

Sugar in the sugar tin.
   Water in the tap.
Fill the pitcher to the brim.
   Hold it in your lap.

When it's full enough you'll feel
   Water down your shin.
That's the time to put a hundred
   Ice cubes in.

Reader Response

Let's Talk

If you had a lemonade sale, how would you get people to come?

Let's Think

The children use a bar graph in the story. How did it help them?

Test Prep
Let's Write

Write a news story about the children's lemonade sale. Give your story a headline. Read your story to the class.

Make a Poster

Pretend you are having a lemonade sale. Make a poster telling about your sale.

1. Draw an interesting picture that will make people stop and buy your lemonade.

2. Write what you plan to do with the money.

3. Show how much each cup of lemonade will cost.

4. Compare your poster with a classmate's poster.

Language Arts

Sentences

A **sentence** is a group of words that tells a complete idea. There are four kinds of sentences: **statement, command, question,** and **exclamation.** Begin every sentence with a capital letter.

Put a **.** at the end of a statement and a command.

The car wash is today.
Wash each window carefully.

Put a **?** at the end of a question.
How much does it cost?

Put an **!** at the end of an exclamation.
The dog is getting us wet!

Talk

Tell a story about the picture. Take turns adding sentences to the story. Use the four kinds of sentences.

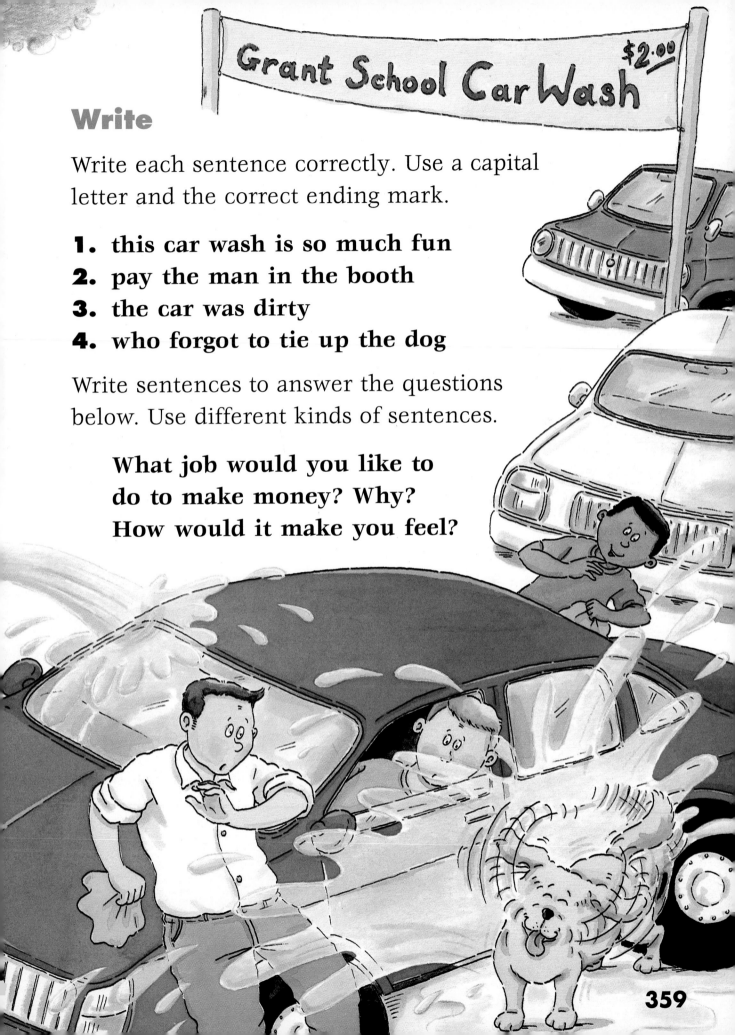

Write

Write each sentence correctly. Use a capital letter and the correct ending mark.

1. this car wash is so much fun
2. pay the man in the booth
3. the car was dirty
4. who forgot to tie up the dog

Write sentences to answer the questions below. Use different kinds of sentences.

What job would you like to do to make money? Why? How would it make you feel?

Start Collecting! It's Fun!

by Joanne Ryder

Shells, dolls, leaves, rocks . . .
  Stamps, coins, trains, clocks . . .

People collect all sorts of things! Maybe you would like to start collecting something too. It can be a great hobby for a young person.

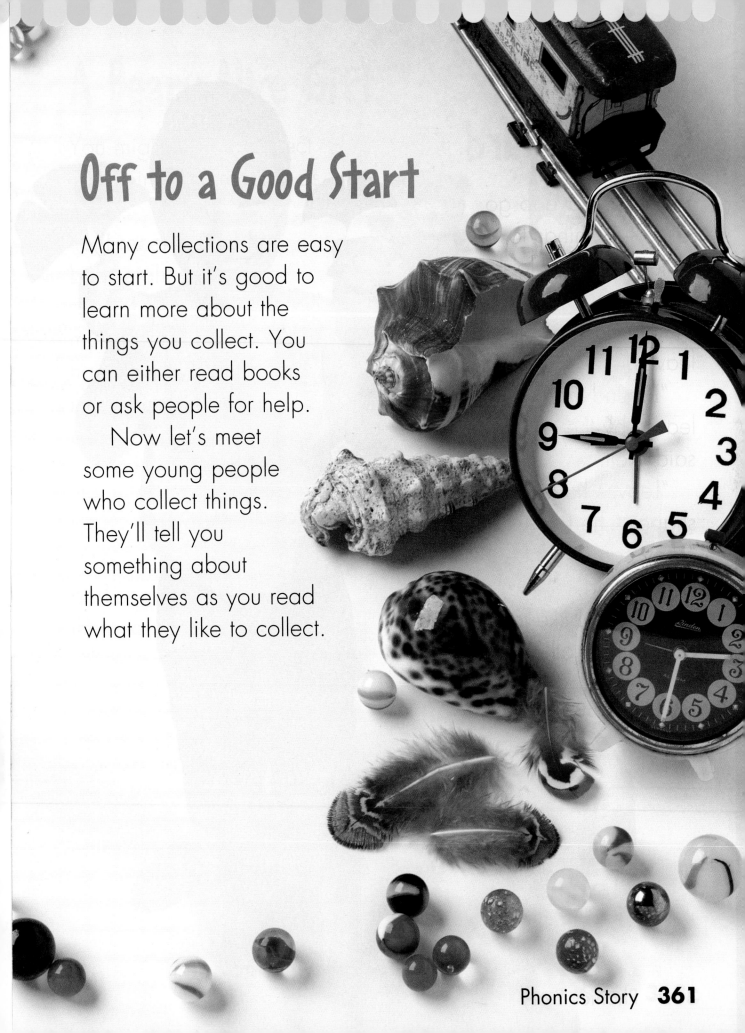

Off to a Good Start

Many collections are easy to start. But it's good to learn more about the things you collect. You can either read books or ask people for help.

Now let's meet some young people who collect things. They'll tell you something about themselves as you read what they like to collect.

A House Full of Hats

"I collect hats," said Jake. "I like funny hats, tall hats, and round hats.

"I receive hats as gifts, either for my birthday or as a surprise," Jake added. "I hang my hats all over the house. I even hang them from the ceiling!

"Once I found a hat on the side of a road," said Jake. "Someone didn't want it, but I did."

Start Collecting!

Choosing a collection is like choosing a friend. Pick one that is good for you.

"Collect what you love," said Sheila. "I love bears, and I love finding new ones."

It is fun to collect. Start now, while you are young, and watch your collection grow and grow.

The Puddle Pail

by Elisa Kleven

One bright morning after a storm, Ernst, a young blue crocodile, and his big green brother, Sol, set off for the beach. They skipped through the wet grass and stamped through the mud, drumming on their shiny pails.

"I'm going to fill my pail with shells," said Sol, who loved to collect things.

"I'm going to fill my pail with sand and build a sand castle," said Ernst, who loved to make things.

"Maybe I'll find some rocks too," said Sol, "all shapes and colors, for my rock collection. And some feathers, for my feather collection, and maybe some string." Sol bent down to pick up a rubber band. "Just the thing for my rubber band collection! You ought to start a collection, Ernst."

"I don't know what to collect," Ernst replied.

"Collect something you really like," said Sol. "Something that comes in all different sizes and colors and shapes. That way your collection will be interesting."

Ernst watched the clouds make flower shapes and sea horse shapes in the windy sky. He watched a little snake cloud puff up into a dragon. He watched a rabbit cloud curl into a ball.

"Clouds are interesting," he said. "I wish I could collect clouds."

"Clouds!" exclaimed Sol. "You can't collect clouds! Think of something else you like."

Just then, something caught Sol's eye—a bottle cap lying in a puddle. "Look at that sparkly bottle cap, Ernst. You could start a bottle cap collection!"

"It's pretty," Ernst agreed. "But I like the puddle it's in even more."

"The puddle?" said Sol.

"It looks like a little piece of sky on the ground. I wish I could collect *it*."

"You can't collect puddles," said Sol.

"Yes, I can collect puddles," said Ernst. "They're not too far away or too big or too hot—and I don't want to eat them." *Splish-splash,* Ernst scooped the puddle into his pail.

"Ernst," said Sol, "you're not really going to start a puddle collection, are you?"

373

"Yes," said Ernst. "I am." He scooped up a green puddle, round as a saucer. *Splash-splosh,* it joined the other puddle in the pail.

Sol rolled his eyes. "Since you're going to stay here collecting puddles, I'll go down to the beach by myself and collect *real* things."

Puddles are real, thought Ernst, as he searched for more to collect. "Here's a purple puddle . . .

and a striped one

and a flowered one.

Here's a puddle full of diamonds and a puddle full of squares . . .

a puddle full of gumballs and a puddle full of brooms, a puddle like an Easter egg,

a puddle like a wheel, and a puddle with a pretzel in it.

Slippery puddles, smooth puddles, lemony, lettery cool puddles." Ernst sang a song as he scooped the puddles up. *Splish-splash* sang the puddles as they slid into the pail.

Sol came back with his pail piled high. "Look what I got, Ernst! Twelve seashells,

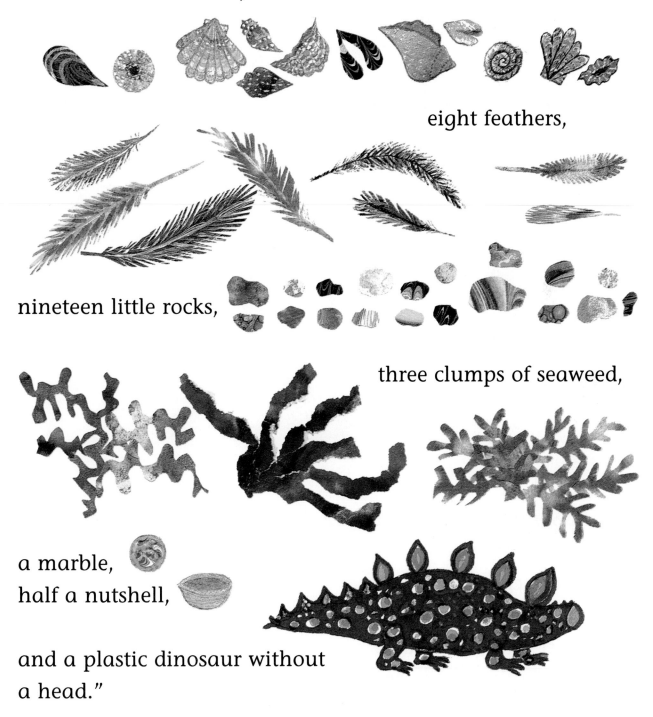

eight feathers,

nineteen little rocks,

three clumps of seaweed,

a marble,
half a nutshell,

and a plastic dinosaur without a head."

"I got a lot of puddles," Ernst announced. "All different sizes and colors and shapes."

Sol peered into Ernst's pail. "Your puddles have all run together! They look like a pail full of ordinary water!"

"They're one *big* puddle now," said Ernst. "An Ernst and Sol puddle!"

"That's the weirdest collection I've ever heard of," Sol replied. "What can you do with a puddle?"

"I'll think of something." Ernst carried his pail carefully as they started for home.

"I know!" said Sol. "You can help me wash the sand off all my new collections."

"You can wash your own collections," Ernst replied. "I'll think of something else to do with my puddle."

Ernst set his puddle pail on the grass and sat down to swing. While he swung, his puddle slowly turned from gold to pink. Clouds swam in and out of it like fishes.

When night fell, stars collected in the puddle pail—and a little piece of the moon too.

Early the next morning, Ernst went out to check on his pail. A thirsty dog was drinking from it. "You like my magic puddle soup?" Ernst asked. The dog wagged her tail and drank some more, leaving Ernst just enough water to paint some watercolor pictures.

Ernst painted the dog,

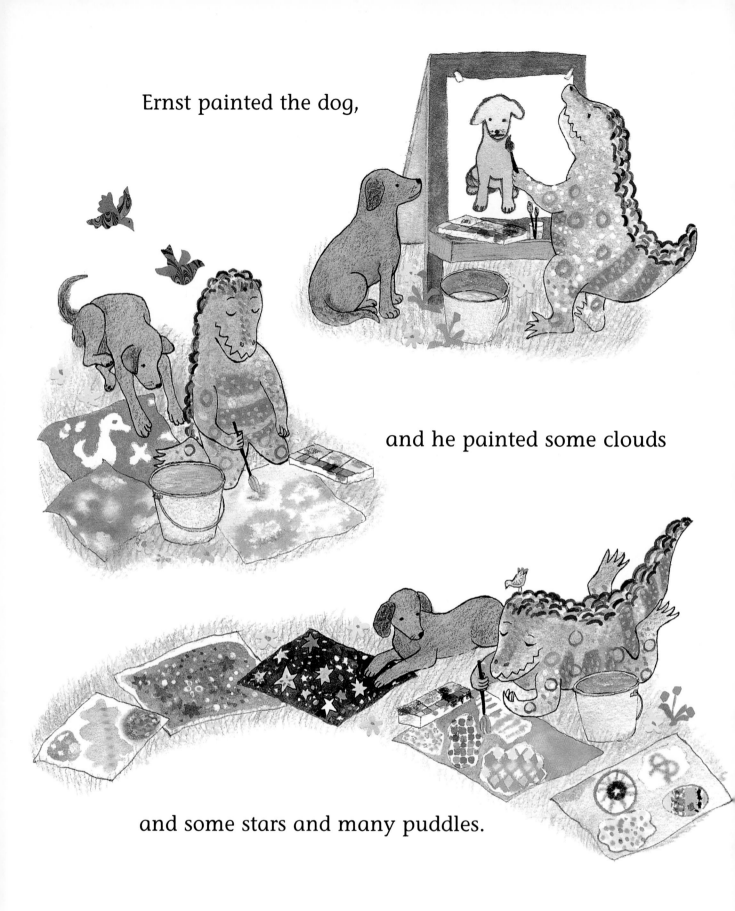

and he painted some clouds

and some stars and many puddles.

Sol came by, his pail filled with flowers and acorns and leaves. "I started some new collections," he said. "What have you got there, Ernst?"

"A dog," replied Ernst. "And a painting collection."

"Oooh!" said Sol. "What a collection! With clouds and stars and everything."

"I used part of my puddle collection to make it," Ernst explained. "The dog drank the other part."

Ernst petted the dog. He looked at the clouds and the stars and the puddles shining on the grass. He felt proud and happy—and hungry too, since he hadn't eaten breakfast yet.

"Let's go collect blackberries," he said, "from the bushes down the road."

"Good idea!" Sol grabbed his pail. "Maybe we'll find some pennies on the way, and some pinecones and gum wrappers."

"And maybe some shadows too," said Ernst.

"Shadows!" said Sol. "You can't—"

"Yes, I can collect shadows!" Ernst cried. He caught one for a second in his pail.

And when it fluttered off, he and Sol filled their pails—and themselves—with sweet, juicy blackberries.

About the Author/Illustrator
Elisa Kleven

Elisa Kleven enjoys collecting things, just like her characters Ernst and Sol.

Ms. Kleven places real objects, such as lace and wool, into her artwork. She likes to "experiment, arrange, rearrange, and discover joyful surprises" as she works. "I love to snip and glue scraps of this and that into new shapes," she says.

Creating her characters reminds Ms. Kleven of playing with toys!

Reader Response

Let's Talk

If you could collect anything from the story, what would you collect?

Let's Think

Why does Ernst think he is collecting clouds, stars, and a piece of the moon in his puddle pail?

Test Prep
Let's Write

Do you like to collect things like Sol, or do you like to make things like Ernst? Choose one character to write a letter to. Tell him what you like to do.

Make a Puddle Pail

Ernst says he collects clouds, stars, and a
piece of the moon with his puddle pail.
He also paints pictures. What can
you do with a puddle pail?

1. Find a pail and fill it with water.
2. Place the pail under a light.
3. Hold objects above the pail.
   Tell friends what you see.
4. Add food coloring to a cup of the water.
   Paint a picture. Share it with classmates.

Language Arts

Quotation Marks

Quotation marks " " show the beginning and end of what someone says.

Miles asked, "What is your favorite stamp?" "This one," said Billy.

Talk

Tell a classmate what the children in the pictures might say about their collections. When someone is speaking, hold up your fingers in the shape of quotation marks.

Write

Write the sentences correctly. Put " at the beginning of what someone says. Put " at the end of what someone says.

1. **Jenny said, Look I found a button on the floor.**
2. **My beads are beautiful! Mia exclaimed.**

Write a story with two characters. Have the characters talk about things they like to collect. Use quotation marks.

Stone Soup

a folktale retold by Lily Toy Hong

One day a peddler crossed a bridge into
a town. He stopped his wagon and sat down on
a rock. The peddler was hungry. He asked a fair
lady if she had any spare food.

"I don't mean to be unkind," she said, "but
we don't have food for ourselves."

390

The peddler took a big black pot from his wagon. "I can make stone soup for us to share."

The lady just stared. "Stone soup?"

"You'll see," said the peddler. "First I need water."

The lady got some water. The peddler filled the pot and lit a fire.

By this time a crowd had come to the town square. "There is nothing like a rare bowl of stone soup!"said the peddler.

He pulled out a small stone. He tossed it over the edge of the pot. "Now we wait," said the peddler.

"Wait if you dare," said the butcher. "But you'll never get soup."

The peddler stirred and sniffed the air. "This soup I'm making will be fine," he said. "But it would taste even better with beets."

A woman stepped up to the edge of the pot. She held up a pair of beets. She said, "Add these to the soup, if you care to." The peddler threw them into the pot.

"This soup I'm making smells good," he said. "But it would taste even better with potatoes."

A boy with red hair said, "I found two potatoes! You can add both."

The peddler dropped in the potatoes. "If only we had a carrot," he said.

"These are from my garden," a woman said.

The peddler licked his lips. He put in the carrots. Then he said, "Onions would add flavor to this soup I'm making."

"I will share my onions," a man said. The peddler added them to the soup.

The air filled with a delicious smell. "This stone soup I'm making is good. But it would taste even better if it had some beef."

"I guess I can give you some," grumbled the butcher. He put some beef into the pot.

At last the peddler took a taste. He smiled and said, "This stone soup I am making is the best of any I have ever prepared."

"I'll be the judge of that!" shouted the butcher. He took a taste and smiled. "The peddler is right!"

The peddler dished out a fair share to everyone. They ate until there wasn't any left. That night the peddler left without a care. And long after, the people talked about the man who made soup from a stone.

Stone Soup

by The Children's Television Workshop
illustrated by Eileen Mueller Neill

Characters

Narrator	Sal Lamie	Rick Cotta
Ida Know	Vida Minn	Frank Furter
Minnie Stronie	Brock Lee	Artie Choke
Ann Chovie	Bill Lownie	

Scene One

Narrator: In the village of Bellie Acres, it was time for the annual "Souper Bowl" contest. The person who created the best soup would receive a soup ladle made of solid gold. The night before the contest, Minnie Stronie called up her best friend, Ann Chovie.

Minnie Stronie: I hope the judges like this year's batch of my famous "Minnie Stronie" soup!

Ann Chovie: Well, I've been cooking all day, and my husband told me my "Ann Chovie" soup is still way too salty!

Minnie Stronie: Did you hear who the judges are? Brock Lee and Sal Lamie. They're tough!

Ann Chovie: I suppose Ida Know will win. She's taken the Golden Ladle three years in a row!

Minnie Stronie: Oh, oh—I've got to go, Ann. My soup is boiling over.

Ann Chovie: Bye, Minnie. Good luck!

Scene Two

Narrator: It's the day of the big contest. Sal Lamie and Brock Lee are tasting the soups. They both stop for second helpings at Ida Know's bowl.

Sal Lamie: This is delicious! What do you call this wonderful soup?

Ida Know: I don't know!

Brock Lee: This soup is both sweet and sour at the same time. What's in it?

Ida Know: I don't know!

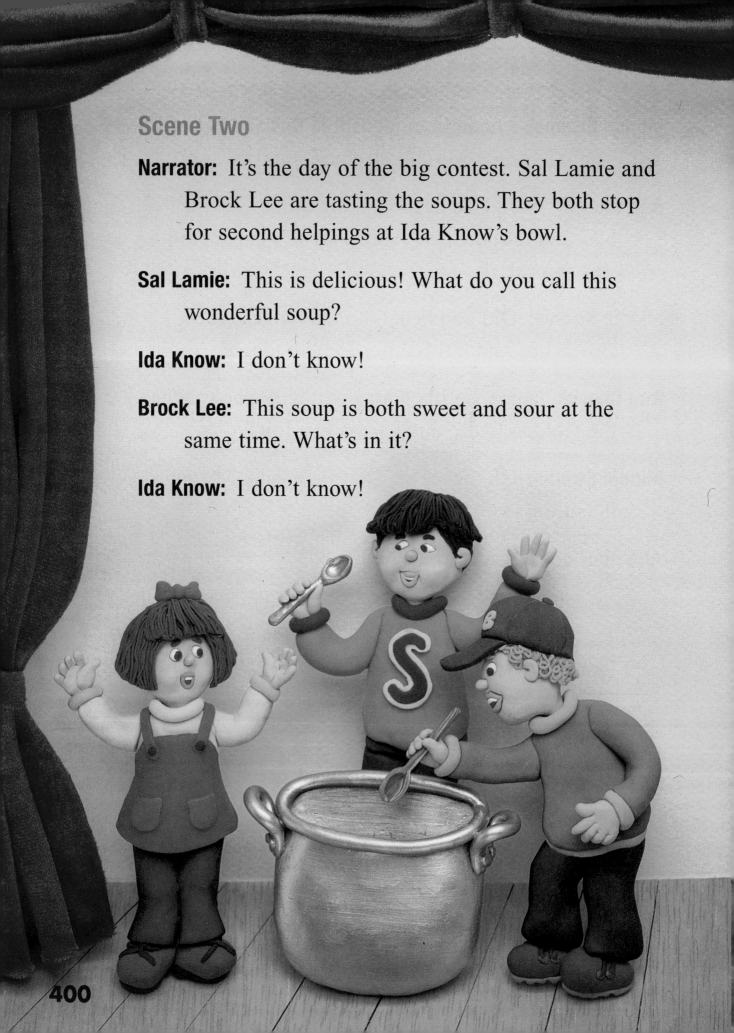

Narrator: Frank Furter was jealous.

Frank Furter: Just once I'd like to be the big wiener—
I mean *winner* at this contest!

Narrator: Vida Minn was angry.

Vida Minn: What's so great about Ida Know's soup?
Now, my soup is good for you! It has vitamins A,
B, and C!

Narrator: The judges were about to declare Ida Know
the winner—when suddenly a stranger appeared
carrying a large black soup kettle.

Stranger: Am I too late? My soup isn't ready yet—but it won't take long to prepare. And I bet it will win!

Sal Lamie: What's your name, sir, and what kind of soup will you make?

Stranger: I'm Bill. Bill Lownie. And I'm making stone soup.

Everyone: STONE SOUP?

Frank Furter: *(to Ida)* How do you make stone soup?

Ida Know: I don't know!

Narrator: Everyone watched as Bill Lownie filled his kettle with water to boil.

Bill: Now I'll just add this ordinary stone. *(He drops a large stone into the kettle. PLUNK!)*

Scene Three

Narrator: Everyone was quiet as Bill Lownie stirred his stone soup. After a little while, he tasted it.

Brock Lee: Well? Is it soup yet?

Bill: I just feel bad I didn't bring a carrot. Stone soup just isn't the same without a little chopped carrot thrown in.

Minnie Stronie: Well, I guess I can spare a carrot. *(She hands him one.)*

Bill: Oh, thank you so much! *(He adds it and stirs for a while, then tastes the soup again.)* Well it's *almost* perfect. This would be the best batch of stone soup I ever made . . . if I only had a potato.

Vida Minn: Here's a potato for you, Mr. Lownie! It's full of Vitamin C!

Bill: You are a kind lady. *(He stirs some more. The aroma of the soup begins to grow.)* Now let's see . . . You know, my mom always added a little scrap of fresh meat. I don't suppose any of you . . .

Frank Furter: *(handing Bill some meat)* Help yourself!

Bill: Now just a little salt and pepper . . .

Ann Chovie: I have those! *(She hands them to him.)*

Bill: And some garlic . . . maybe an onion.

Minnie Stronie: *(whispering)* Ask Artie Choke if he brought any garlic with him. And I think Rick Cotta has an onion.

Artie Choke: *(handing over garlic)* Good luck, pal!

Rick Cotta: Here's your onion. And I brought you a little grated cheese too.

Ann Chovie: *(sniffing)* Mmm! Doesn't the stone soup smell delicious?

Frank Furter: It sure does!

Bill: It just has to cook a little bit more.

Narrator: Finally, Sal Lamie and Brock Lee tasted the stone soup.

Sal Lamie: This is magnificent!

After the children left for school, Momma would turn on the radio. Momma swayed with the sweet rhythm as she sipped her coffee.

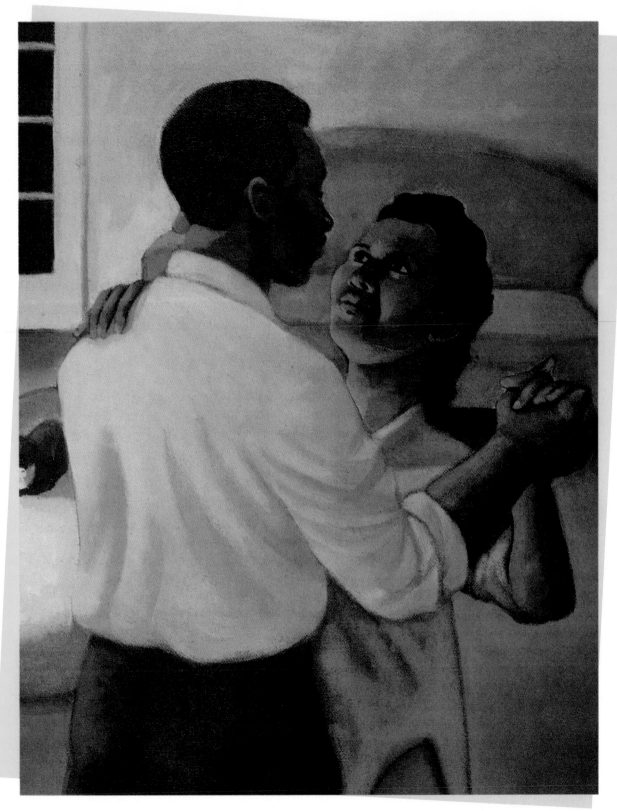

Every night, after the children were in bed, Daddy would say, "Come on, honey! Let's go once around the floor." Then he and Momma slow danced to the soulful, blues music he loved.

Lee loved music so much that he joined his school band. Annie thought Lee looked wonderful in his uniform with the shiny brass buttons. Lee's music sounded like the circus. When he swung into a song on the trumpet, Annie tapped her feet and clapped her hands.

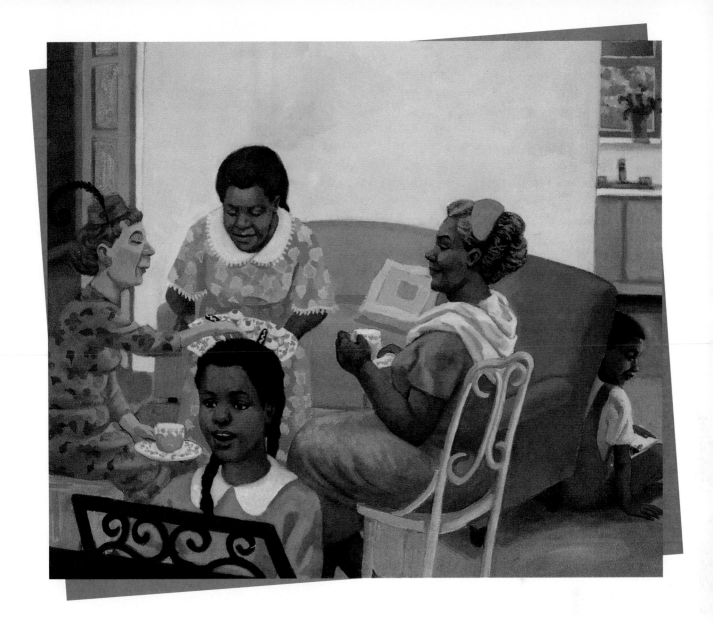

Patty was a wonderful musician too. When Patty
played the piano it made Annie think of pretty
colors, soft rain, and springtime flowers. Patty also
had a lovely singing voice. When company came,
she would entertain the guests.

"Wonderful, just wonderful," the guests
would sigh and clap their hands after Patty's
performance. Annie decided that she wanted to
play an instrument too.

One day, Annie's school music teacher, Mrs. Mason, passed out instruments to the class. She gave Annie a recorder.

The class practiced a group song for months. Everyone played their part perfectly, everyone, except Annie. When Annie played, the recorder squeaked and squawked like chickens at feeding time.

"I don't think the recorder is the instrument for you," Mrs. Mason said.

"I guess you're right," Annie said. "Maybe I can play the cello."

"Let's give it a try," Mrs. Mason said. "I'll show you how to play it."

When Mrs. Mason played the cello, it sounded warm and carefree, like carousel music. Annie tried and tried, but when she played the cello, it always sounded like a chorus of screeching alley cats.

"Oh," Mrs. Mason sighed and rubbed her ears. "Annie, darling, I just don't think this is the instrument for you. How would you like to make a banner and some posters announcing our program?"

"Okay," said Annie. She was disappointed, but she did love to draw. Annie drew while everyone else practiced.

That evening, Annie picked up Lee's trumpet and tried to play it. Her playing sounded like an elephant with a bad cold. Lee begged her to stop. Annie's feelings were hurt, but she put the trumpet away.

"I wish I could find an instrument to play," Annie told her mother.

"Cheer up!" Momma said. "We're going to get a new piano and everyone is going to take piano lessons!"

Soon, a beautiful, new piano was delivered to Annie's house. The piano was made of shiny, brown mahogany. Annie peeked under the piano lid while Patty played a song. "Melody Maker" was written in beautiful gold letters.

That week, all three children started piano lessons with Mrs. Kelly. After every lesson, Mrs. Kelly gave them new sheet music to practice.

Patty and Lee did very well. Mrs. Kelly always told them how talented they were.

Oh, but when Annie played the piano, Mrs. Kelly's smile turned into a frown. The low notes sounded like a diesel truck honking its horn, the middle ones like croaking frogs, and the high notes sobbed like a crying baby.

Once, Annie tried to sing and play the piano for her parents' guests. Her performance made everyone squirm in their chairs. Annie was so embarrassed that she went up to her room and cried. She couldn't play the recorder or the cello. She couldn't play the piano or sing or play the trumpet. Annie had never felt so sad in her life.

Sometimes, when Annie was sad, she liked to write poetry to make herself feel better. She decided to write a poem about music.

> *I love to hear music play.*
> *I practice hard every day.*
> *But even though I try and try,*
> *the sounds I play*
> *make people laugh and cry.*

That night, Annie put her poem on Daddy's pillow. Then she went to sleep.

In the morning, Daddy and Momma had a long talk with Annie.

"I just can't seem to do anything right," Annie sighed.

"Yes, you can," Daddy said. "There are lots of things you can do."

"Really, Daddy?" Annie asked.

"Of course," Momma said. "Not everyone can play the piano and sing like Patty. Not everyone can play the trumpet like Lee. That's his special gift. And not everyone can write poetry and draw beautiful pictures the way you can."

"I didn't think about it that way," Annie said. "I can't sing or play an instrument well, but I can do *a lot* of other things."

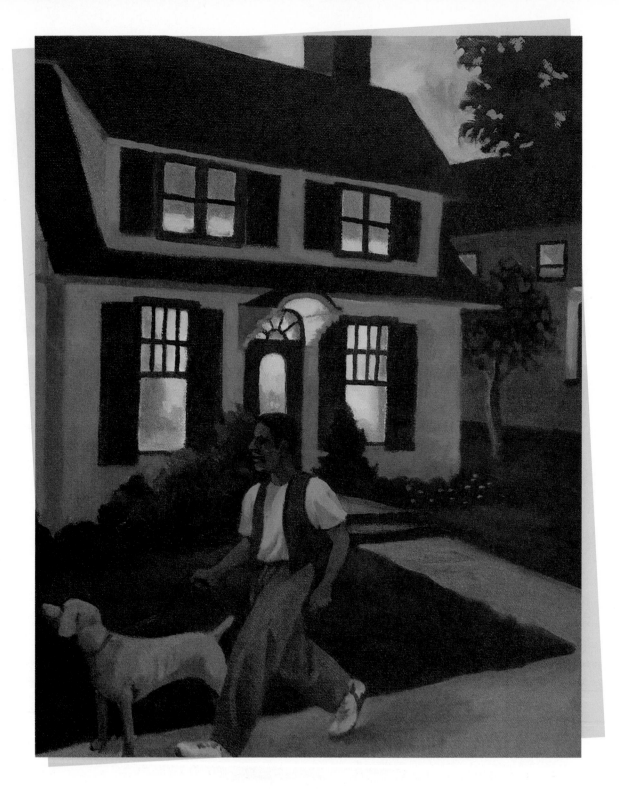

Now, if you should pass by Annie's house, you might hear Patty singing and playing on the piano. Perhaps you'll hear Lee playing his trumpet. And sometimes, if you stop and listen very, very closely, you might hear Annie playing . . .

her radio!

Annie plays loud, finger-popping music when she feels like laughing and drawing pictures. She plays soft, sweet music when she writes her poems. She can play any kind of music she likes on her radio.

She still can't play the piano or sing like Patty, and she still can't play the trumpet like Lee.

But now Annie has found she's happiest when drawing her pictures and writing poetry. Because art and writing are Annie's gifts.

About the Author
Angela Shelf Medearis

Angela Shelf Medearis wrote *Annie's Gifts* for her older sister and younger brother. She based the book on her own childhood. Like Annie, Ms. Medearis discovered early that she had a talent that brought her great joy. Ms. Medearis also loves to read. She especially enjoys reading picture books, which she says are "a child's first step into a lifetime of reading."

About the Illustrator
Anna Rich

Anna Rich discovered her talents as an artist when she was very young. Even in kindergarten, she enjoyed both drawing and coloring.

Remember

by Nikki Grimes

I remember that time
I stood on stage
at the Countee Cullen Library
and recited my poem
and hardly noticed
how loudly my knees
were knocking
'cause you were there
smiling from the front row
to let me know
that I was doing
just fine.

Reader Response

Let's Talk

If you could choose a talent, what would it be?

Let's Think

Why do you think Annie left the poem for her father to read?

Test Prep
Let's Write

What did Annie learn about people's gifts? Write about the lesson she learned.

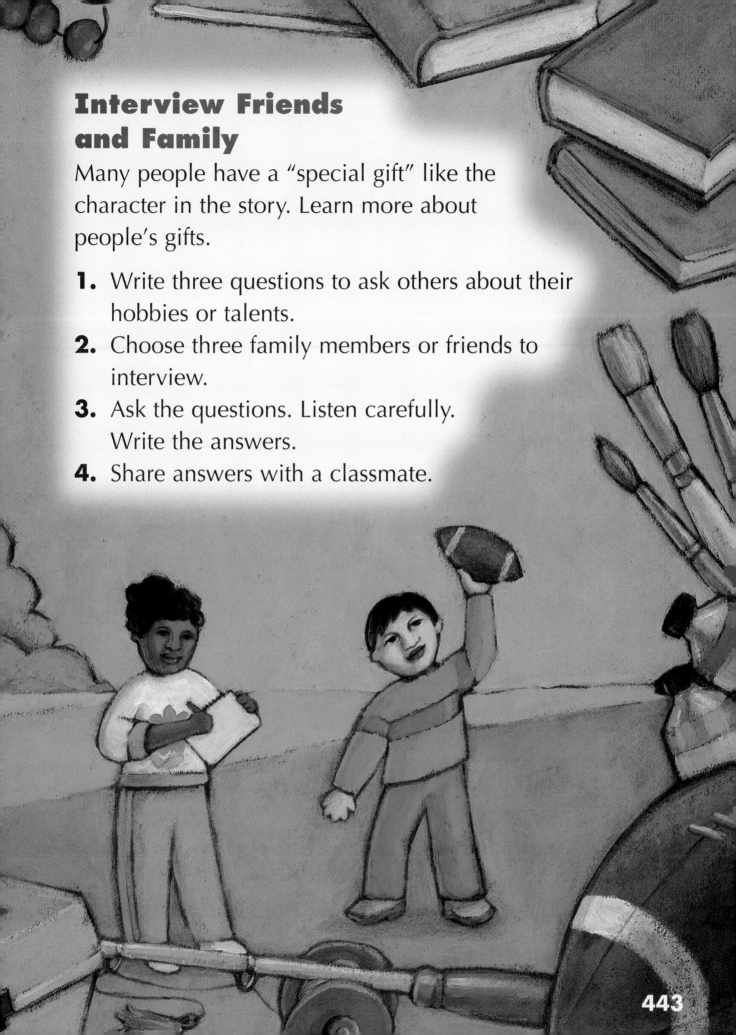

Interview Friends and Family

Many people have a "special gift" like the character in the story. Learn more about people's gifts.

1. Write three questions to ask others about their hobbies or talents.
2. Choose three family members or friends to interview.
3. Ask the questions. Listen carefully. Write the answers.
4. Share answers with a classmate.

443

Language Arts

More About Commas

Sometimes two sentences are joined together by connecting words such as **and, but,** and **so.** Use a comma before the connecting word.

Mike loves to draw. He loves to paint.
Mike loves to draw, **and** he loves to paint.

Nola cannot paint. She can play the violin.
Nola cannot paint, **but** she can play the violin.

Gary's arm is tired. He will let it rest.
Gary's arm is tired, **so** he will let it rest.

Talk

Make up sentences that have the connecting words **and, but,** and **so.** Tell the sentences to your classmates. Tell where you would put a comma.

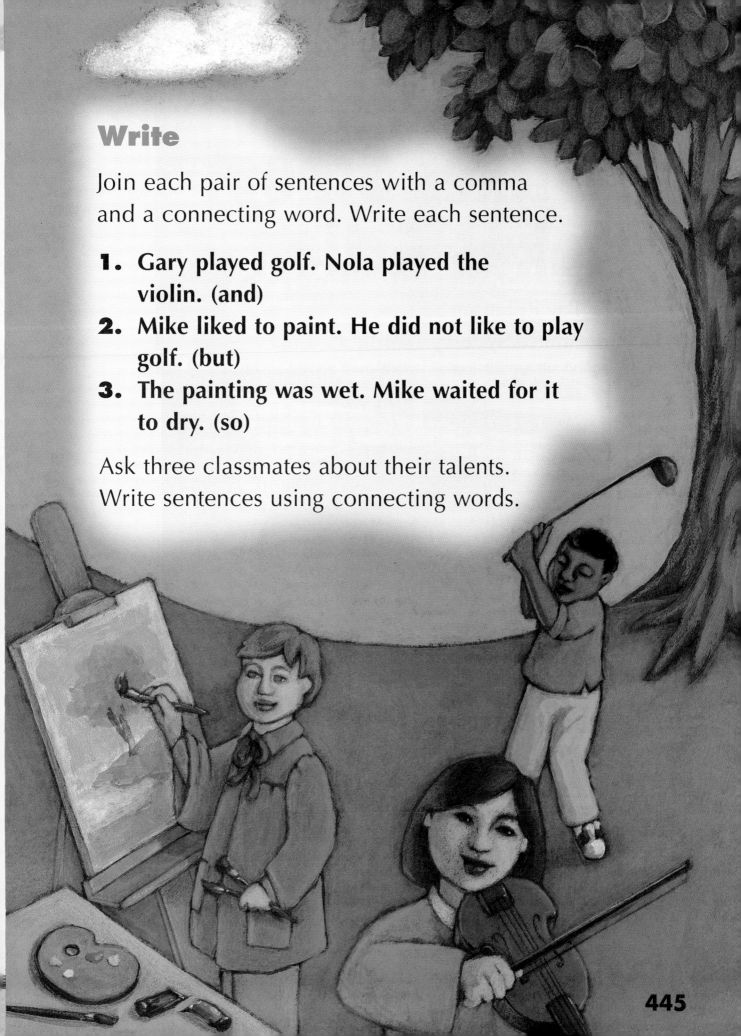

Write

Join each pair of sentences with a comma and a connecting word. Write each sentence.

1. Gary played golf. Nola played the violin. (and)
2. Mike liked to paint. He did not like to play golf. (but)
3. The painting was wet. Mike waited for it to dry. (so)

Ask three classmates about their talents. Write sentences using connecting words.

Wicker School students meet Mayor Lopez.

Students Take Action

"Earl had information about a mural painted by children in Chicago. Earl thought kids from our school could learn to paint a mural under the bridge," said Mrs. Pearl.

Wicker School took action. First, they asked people to sign a petition. Then they went to the mayor. Mrs. Pearl and her students waited for two hours at city hall. "Nothing was going to stop us," she said.

M

S

V

s

N

l

S

S

The children draw their plan.

Mayor Lopez gave the okay. In addition, she asked them not to take action until spring vacation.

With Mrs. Pearl's help, children used markers and a large piece of paper to make their plan. In addition, they used rulers and other tools.

How Students Earned Money

Wicker School students set up collection boxes and sold candy. They earned enough money to buy paint, brushes, and the clean-up supplies for the project.

Children set up collection boxes to raise money.

City Green

by DyAnne DiSalvo-Ryan

There used to be a building right here on this lot. It was three floors up and down, an empty building nailed up shut for as long as I could remember. My friend Miss Rosa told me Old Man Hammer used to live there—some other neighbors too. But when I asked him about that, he only hollered, "Scram."

Old Man Hammer seems hard as nails.

Last year two people from the city came by, dressed in suits and holding papers. They said, "This building is unsafe. It will have to be torn down."

By winter a crane with a wrecking ball was parked outside. Mama gathered everyone to watch from our front window. In three slow blows that building was knocked into a heap of pieces. Then workers took the rubble away in a truck and filled the hole with dirt.

Now this block looks like a big smile with one tooth missing. Old Man Hammer sits on his stoop and shakes his head. "Look at that piece of junk land on a city block," Old Man Hammer says. "Once that building could've been saved. But nobody even tried."

And every day when I pass this lot it makes me sad to see it.

Then spring comes, and right on schedule Miss
Rosa starts cleaning her coffee cans. Miss Rosa and
I keep coffee cans outside our windowsills. Every
year we buy two packets of seeds at the hardware
store—sometimes marigolds, sometimes zinnias,
and one time we tried tomatoes. We go to the park,
scoop some dirt, and fill up the cans halfway.

Saturday morning I'm up with the sun and looking at this lot. My mama looks out too. "Marcy," she says, and hugs me close. "Today I'm helping you and Rosa."

After shopping, Mama empties her grocery bags and folds them flat to carry under her arm. "Come on, Mrs. B.," Mama tells her friend. "We're going to clear this lot."

Then what do you know but my brother comes along. My brother is tall and strong. At first, he scratches his neck and shakes his head just like Old Man Hammer. But Mama smiles and says, "None of that here!" So all day long he piles junk into those bags and carries them to the curb.

Now, this time of day is early. Neighbors pass by and see what we're doing. Most say, "We want to help too." They have a little time to spare. Then this one calls that one and that one calls another.

"Come on and help," I call to Old Man Hammer.

"I'm not helping anybody," he hollers. "You're all wasting your time."

Sour grapes my mama'd say, and sour grapes is right.

Just before supper, when we are good and hungry, my mama looks around this lot. "Marcy," she says, "you're making something happen here."

Next day the city drops off tools like rakes and brooms, and a Dumpster for trash. Now there are even more neighbors to help. Miss Rosa, my brother, and I say "Good morning" to Old Man Hammer, but Old Man Hammer just waves like he's swatting a fly.

"Why is Old Man Hammer so mean and cranky these days?" my brother asks.

"Maybe he's really sad," I tell him. "Maybe he misses his building."

"That rotten old building?" My brother shrugs. "He should be happy the city tore down that mess."

"Give him time," Miss Rosa says. "Good things take time."

Mr. Bennett brings wood—old slats he's saved—
and nails in a cup. "I knew all along I saved them
for something," he says. "This wood's good wood."

Then Mr. Rocco from two houses down comes,
carrying two cans of paint. "I'll never use these," he
says. "The color's too bright. But here, this lot could
use some brightening up."

Well, anyone can tell with all the excitement that something is going on. And everyone has an idea about what to plant—strawberries, carrots, lettuce, and more. Tulips and daisies, petunias, and more! Sonny turns the dirt over with a snow shovel. Even Leslie's baby tries to dig with a spoon.

For lunch, Miss Rosa brings milk and jelly and bread and spreads a beach towel where the junk is cleared. By the end of the day a fence is built and painted as bright as the sun.

Later, Mama kisses my cheek and closes my bedroom door. By the streetlights I see Old Man Hammer come down his steps to open the gate and walk into the back of this lot. He bends down quick, sprinkling something from his pocket and covering it over with dirt.

In the morning I tell my brother. "Oh, Marcy," he says. "You're dreaming. You're wishing too hard."

But I know what I saw, and I tell my mama, "Old Man Hammer's planted some seeds."

Right after breakfast, I walk to the back of this lot. And there it is—a tiny raised bed of soil. It is neat and tidy, just like the rows we've planted. Now I know for sure that Old Man Hammer planted something. So I pat the soil for good luck and make a little fence to keep the seeds safe.

Every day I go for a look inside our garden lot. Other neighbors stop in too. One day Mrs. Wells comes by. "This is right where my grandmother's bedroom used to be," she says. "That's why I planted my flowers there."

I feel sad when I hear that. With all the digging and planting and weeding and watering, I'd forgotten about the building that had been on this lot. Old Man Hammer had lived there too. I go to the back, where he planted his seeds. I wonder if this was the place where his room used to be.

I look down. Beside my feet, some tiny stems are sprouting. Old Man Hammer's seeds have grown! I run to his stoop. "Come with me!" I beg, tugging at his hand. "You'll want to see."

I walk him past the hollyhocks, the daisies, the peppers, the rows of lettuce. I show him the strawberries that I planted. When Old Man Hammer sees his little garden bed, his sour grapes turn sweet. "Marcy, child." He shakes his head. "This lot was good for nothing. Now it's nothing but good," he says.

Soon summertime comes, and this lot really grows. It fills with vegetables, herbs, and flowers. And way in the back, taller than anything else, is a beautiful patch of yellow sunflowers. Old Man Hammer comes every day. He sits in the sun, eats his lunch, and sometimes comes back with supper.

Nobody knows how the sunflowers came—not Leslie, my brother, or Miss Rosa. Not Mr. Bennett, or Sonny, or anyone else. But Old Man Hammer just sits there smiling at me. We know whose flowers they are.

About the Author

DyAnne DiSalvo-Ryan

DyAnne DiSalvo-Ryan lives in New York City. She considers the city very important to her work.

"Living in New York City brings my art to life," she says. "When I ride the subways, I sketch the people I see."

Ms. DiSalvo-Ryan remembers clearly the house she lived in as a girl. She loved her Brooklyn neighborhood. Both influenced her work.

Reader Response

Let's Talk

What other things could you do with an empty lot?

Let's Think

Why did Marcy keep Old Man Hammer's secret about the flowers?

Test Prep
Let's Write

Pretend that you are starting a community garden. Write a letter to neighbors and friends asking for their help. Give three reasons why a community garden would be good for your neighborhood.

Make a Mural

Imagine what the garden looks like in the story. Work with friends to make a garden mural. Use it to brighten up your classroom.

1. Look through books about flowers and plants. Find colorful and interesting plants and flowers.
2. Use a large sheet of paper, paint, markers, and colored paper to create the garden.
3. Hang your garden mural on a wall.

Paragraphs

A **paragraph** is a group of sentences about the same idea. The first word starts a few spaces from the left.

> **My class will plant a garden this spring. Our parents are giving us seeds to plant. The principal said we could plant the garden in front of the school. I can't wait to see the flowers grow!**

Look at the first sentence. It tells the main idea. The other sentences tell more about the main idea. When you write a paragraph, make sure your sentences are about the main idea.

Talk

Talk about the picture. What is the main idea? Say it in a sentence. Take turns adding sentences about the main idea.

Write

Write the paragraph. Leave out the sentences that are not about the main idea.

It is easy to plant a flower. First, you need a seed. Then you need to plant the seed in dirt. Sally got dirt on her pants! Finally, you need to water your seed. Water is very good for you. Make sure you put your plant in sunlight.

Write a paragraph about something you have done. Your first sentence should tell the main idea. Your other sentences should tell more about the main idea.

The Clubhouse

Lemonade for Sale

above

few

ice

kept

number

sound

Start Collecting! It's Fun!

The Puddle Pail

castle

crocodile

eight

puddle

road

round

shadows

young

Stone Soup

Stone Soup

add
both
contest
delicious
judges
making
mean
stranger

Wicker School Takes Action

City Green

already
empty
nothing
piece
soil
used

A Good Idea

Annie's Gifts

also
group
radio
squeaked
though
tried

poetry

Test Talk

Write Your Answer

Some test questions ask you to write the answer. You will need to look back at the story to find the answer. You must use words from the story to write your answer correctly.

Read these paragraphs and a question about *Annie's Gifts.*

> Annie was so embarrassed that she went up to her room and cried. She couldn't play the recorder or cello. She couldn't play the piano or sing or play the trumpet. Annie had never felt so sad in her life.
>
> Sometimes, when Annie was sad, she liked to write poetry to make herself feel better. She decided to write a poem about music.

1. What did Annie do to make herself feel better? Write your answer.

What is the question asking? Find the words in the paragraphs to write your answer.

Here is how one boy chose his answer.

I need to find out what Annie does to make herself feel better. One paragraph says that Annie wrote poetry to make herself feel better. I will use those words to write my answer.

Try it!

Use what you learned to answer this question about *Annie's Gifts*. Look at page 436 to find words to write your answer.

2. What are Annie's gifts? Write your answer.

Glossary

Words from Your Stories

Aa

above

a·ble
If you are **able** to do something, you have the power to do it: *Some animals are **able** to see well in the dark.*

a·bove
*The sun is **above** the hills. Read the line **above** the picture.*

add
To **add** is to put numbers or things together: **Add** *5 and 3 to make 8. The cook will **add** two more eggs to the batter.*

a·go
Ago means in the past: *I saw him two weeks **ago**. Long **ago** people lived in caves.*

al·read·y
*She ran to the bus stop, but the bus had **already** gone. He has **already** read this book.*

al·so
*Tom has a dog, but he likes cats **also**. Sara likes to ride her bike to school, but she **also** likes to walk.*

at·ten·tion

When you give something or someone **attention**, you are giving it thought or care: *Pay* **attention** *while she explains this math problem. The boy gives his dog a lot of* **attention**.

Bb

beach

beach

A **beach** is an area of land found next to a body of water. A **beach** is covered with sand or stones.

behind

be·gan

She **began** *to sing. Snow* **began** *to fall.*

be·hind

He is walking **behind** *her. Her class is* **behind** *in its work.*

both

Both *houses are pink.* **Both** *dogs are mine.*

brook

A **brook** is a small stream of running water. Another word for **brook** is **creek**.

Cc

calm

When someone or something is **calm**, they are quiet or still: *The lake is* **calm** *today. She was frightened, but she answered with a* **calm** *voice. Please* **calm** *down.*

castle

cas·tle

A **castle** is a large building with thick walls and a tower, or something like it: *The king lives in a* **castle**. *We made a sand* **castle**.

cir·cled

When you have **circled** something, you have gone around it in a ring: *The plane* **circled** *the airport until the fog lifted and it was able to land. The spaceship* **circled** *Earth.*

claws

Claws are the sharp, curved nails on the foot of an animal or bird.

con·test

A **contest** is something you enter to win a prize. **Contests** can be between two people or many people: *I entered a cooking* **contest**.

course

A **course** is the direction taken: *After reading the compass, the captain decided to take a* **course** *straight north.*

crea·ture

A **creature** is any living person or animal: *We fed the lost dog because the poor* **creature** *was hungry.*

croc·o·dile

A **crocodile** is a large animal with thick skin, four short legs, and a pointed nose. A **crocodile** looks a lot like an alligator.

crocodile

crops

Crops are plants grown by farmers for food. *Corn and wheat are important* **crops** *in the United States.*

Dd

deck

deck

A **deck** is one of the floors of a ship. A **deck** divides a ship into different levels.

de·li·cious

When something is **delicious**, it tastes or smells very good: *The cookies were* **delicious**.

dif·fer·ent

Different means not alike: *Leaves have* **different** *shapes. Basketball is* **different** *from baseball.*

dock

A **dock** is a platform built at the edge of the water. Ships load and unload at a **dock**.

Ee

ear·ly

1 **Early** means near the beginning of something: **Early** *in the school year, the children didn't know each other very well.*
2 **Early** also means before the usual time: *She got up* **early** *yesterday morning.*

Earth

Earth

Earth is the planet we live on. The planet **Earth** moves around the sun.

485

edge

An **edge** is the line or place where something ends: *We stopped at the edge of town.*

eight

Eight is one more than seven; 8.

empty

emp·ty

When something is **empty**, there is nothing inside: *She finished her cereal and left the empty bowl. We played in an empty lot.*

ev·er

Is he ever at home? When will she ever get here?

fam·i·ly

1 A **family** is a father, mother, and their children. The people who you live with and who take care of you are your **family**.
2 Your **family** is also all of your relatives: *Grandmother invited the family for Thanksgiving dinner.*

feathers

feath·ers

Feathers are the light, soft things that cover a bird's body.

few

1 Few means not many: *Few people came to the meeting.*
2 A **few** is a small number: *Pick the ripe apples and take a few to your grandparents.*

fi·nal·ly

Finally means at last: *Our team* **finally** *won a game.*

float·ing

floating

When something or someone is **floating**, they are moving slowly on top of the water or in the air. *The balloon was* **floating** *through the air. The jellyfish was* **floating** *in the sea.*

flopped

When you have **flopped**, you have dropped or fallen down in a heavy way: *Mother was so tired she* **flopped** *into a chair.*

front

1 The **front** is the part of anything that faces forward: *The dog stood on its* **front** *feet.*
2 The **front** is also the first part or beginning: *Move to the* **front** *of the line.*

Gg

gath·ered

gathered

When you have **gathered** something, you have collected things or brought things together. When people come together, they have **gathered**: *Tom* **gathered** *his tools and went to fix his bike. The crowd* **gathered** *to hear the speaker.*

giant

gi·ant

When something is **giant**, it is very big: *I made a **giant** sandwich for lunch and shared it with my brothers. The dinosaur made **giant** tracks.* Another word for **giant** is **huge**.

group

1 A **group** is a number of people or things together: *We saw a **group** of children playing.*
2 To **group** means to gather a number of people or things together: *I **grouped** the pictures of all the cats on one page.*

grow

To **grow** is to get bigger: *A cactus will **grow** in sand. When I **grow** up I want to be a teacher.*

growl

To **growl** is to make a deep or angry sound: *The dog **growled** at the squirrels. My stomach is **growling**.*

Hh

head, *def. 1*

head

1 The **head** is the top part of the human body, or the front part of most animal bodies. The **head** is where the eyes, ears, nose, mouth, and brain are.
2 The **head** is also the top or front part of something: *We put the pillow at the **head** of the bed. She went to the **head** of the line.*

hel·met

A **helmet** is a covering to protect the head. **Helmets** can be made out of metal, plastic, leather, and other materials.

hos·pi·tal

A **hospital** is a place where sick people are cared for: *Doctors and nurses work in a* **hospital**.

Ii

ice

Ice is frozen water: *The pond turns to* **ice** *in winter. I put some* **ice** *in my lemonade.*

ice

im·por·tant

1 When something is **important**, it has great meaning or value: *It is* **important** *that you learn to read well.*

2 When someone is **important**, that person is famous or powerful: *The President is a very* **important** *person in the United States.*

in·ter·est·ing

When something is **interesting**, it holds your attention: *The book was so* **interesting** *that I did not want to stop reading.*

Jj

judges

1 **Judges** are people who decide questions of right and wrong under the law.

2 **Judges** also decide the winner of a contest: *The* **judges** *gave Grandma's jam a first-place medal.*

judges

489

Kk

kitchen

kept

She **kept** *my secret. He has* **kept** *all their letters. I* **kept** *track of our sales.*

kitch·en

A **kitchen** is a room where food is cooked and stored.

Ll

large

large

Large means big: *We live in a* **large** *apartment* building. **Large** *crowds come to see the team play.*

los·es

When someone **loses**, they do not win: *If our team* **loses** *this game, we won't make it to the finals.*

Mm

mak·ing

1 When you are **making** something, you are putting it together or building it: *We are* **making** *soup for dinner.*

2 When you are **making** something, you can also be causing it to happen: *Please stop* **making** *noise.*

3 When you are **making** money, you are getting money for doing something: *We are* **making** *money selling lemonade.* ● **makes, made, mak•ing.**

mean

1 When you **mean** to do something, you have it in mind as a goal or you want to do it: *He didn't* **mean** *to break the glass.*

2 When one thing **means** another, they are the same: *Automobile* **means** *the same thing as car.* ● means, meant, mean•ing.

morn•ing

1 **Morning** is the part of the day between nighttime and noon: *He got up early this* **morning.**

2 **Morning** also means active or experienced at that time of day: *I am a* **morning** *person.*

morning

Nn

near

When something is **near** it is close, or not far away: *We live* **near** *a lake. My birthday is* **near.**

noth•ing

There was **nothing** *in the empty closet.* **Nothing** *could stop the team from winning.*

num•ber

number, *def. 2*

1 A **number** is a word that tells how many. Two is a **number.** Twenty-one is a **number.**

2 A **number** is also a figure or group of figures that stands for a **number.** 9 is a **number.** 21 is a **number.**

3 To **number** is to give a **number** to: *We will* **number** *the boxes as we fill them.*

Oo

oven

ov·en

The **oven** is the part of a stove that you use to bake things in: *The turkey is in the* **oven.**

own

1 When you **own** something, you have it or keep it because you bought it or because someone gave it to you: *I* **own** *a bicycle.*
2 **Own** also means belonging to you: *I make my* **own** *bed every morning.*

Pp

pa·per

1 **Paper** is what you use to write, print, or draw on. **Paper** is also used for wrapping packages and covering walls. Many bags are made of **paper. Paper** is made from wood.
2 A **paper** is also something with writing or printing on it, such as an essay: *Our teacher collected the* **papers** *we had written.*

piece

piece

A **piece** is one of the parts into which something is divided or broken: *I found the last* **piece** *of the puzzle and will now finish it.*

poke

When you **poke** something, you push against it with force: *He* **poked** *me in the side with his elbow.*

present

pres·ent

A **present** is a gift: *His uncle sent him a birthday* **present**.

prob·a·bly

Probably means likely: *You* **probably** *know my brother. We should* **probably** *wait for them.*

pud·dle

A **puddle** is a small amount of water: *The rain left a big* **puddle** *near the steps.*

 Rr _____

radio

ra·di·o

A **radio** is an electric machine that plays voices and music. A **radio** may be small enough to carry in your pocket.

read·y

When you are **ready**, you are all set to do something. When something is **ready** it has been prepared: *Are they* **ready** *to leave for the movie? Lunch is* **ready**.

re·al·ly

1 **Really** means truly: *Some adventure stories are fun to read, but they could not* **really** *happen.*
2 **Really** also means very: *I am* **really** *hungry.*

re·mem·ber

When you **remember** something, you call it back to your mind: *I can't* **remember** *their address.*

road

road

A **road** is a way to go between places, especially a way for a car, truck, or bus to go along: *This **road** goes to the city.*

rock·ets

Rockets are long metal tubes open at one end. When fuel in the **rockets** is lighted, it burns quickly and drives the rockets forward or straight up. **Rockets** are used to launch spacecraft.

round

Round means shaped like a ball or a circle. The Earth is **round**. A wheel is **round**.

Ss

shadows

se·cret·ly

When something is done **secretly**, it is kept hidden from most people: *We enter our clubhouse **secretly**.*

shad·ows

Shadows are the dark shapes made when something blocks the light.

soil

Soil is the top layer of the ground: *Our garden has such rich **soil** that almost anything will grow in it.* Another word for **soil** is **dirt**.

some·day

Someday means at a future time: ***Someday** we will take a trip to Canada.*

sound

1 A **sound** is something you hear: *He heard the **sound** of a dog barking. What is the **sound** of the a in* hat?

2 To **sound** is to make a **sound** or **sounds**: *The wind **sounds** like a whistle blowing. The words* ate *and* eight ***sound** alike.*

spe·cial

Special means unusual or different in some way: *Your birthday is a **special** day.*

squeaked

When something has **squeaked**, it has made a short, sharp, loud sound: *The chair **squeaked** when I sat on it.*

steers

steers

When a person **steers** something, he or she is causing it to go in a certain direction. A person who **steers** something is guiding or controlling it: *The little cat **steers** the boat.*

still

1 When something is **still**, it is quiet or not moving: *Please keep **still** while I am on the telephone.*

2 **Still** also means up to and including now: *Golf is **still** a popular game.*

stone

stone

> **Stone** is hard rock: *Over time, the ash turned to* **stone.**

sto·ry

> A **story** is words put together that tell about people and places and what happens to them. A **story** can be true or make-believe.

stran·ger

> A s**tranger** is a person you have not known, seen, or heard of before: *After meeting some other kids, she was no longer a* **stranger.**

sure

> When you are **sure**, you are feeling no doubt about something: *Are you* **sure** *you locked the front door?* Another word for **sure** is **certain.**

 Tt

team

team

> A **team** is a group of people working or playing together: *My sister is on the soccer* **team.**

things

> *Please put these* **things** *away. What kind of* **things** *do you do after school?*

though

> **Though** *it looked like rain, we went on our hike anyway. Even* **though** *I tried, I couldn't do it.*

to·day

Today is this day: **Today** *is my uncle's birthday. Are you going swimming* **today?**

told

She **told** *me about the play. Has she* **told** *you about it?*

trade

A **trade** is getting something in return for giving something: *An apple for an orange at lunch today was a fair* **trade.**

trade

tried

He **tried** *to pick up the chair. She has* **tried** *on several pairs of shoes.*

try

If you **try,** you set out to do something if you can: *Let's* **try** *to cut the grass before noon.*

Uu

up·on

Once **upon** *a time there were three elves. The elves sat* **upon** *the bed.* **Upon** *my word, it's true!*

upon

used

1 When something is **used** it is put into service: *I used a brush on my dog's fur.*

2 **Used** also means not new: *My parents bought a* **used** *car.*

used to means once did: *There* **used to** *be a building on this empty lot.*

497

Ww

wash, *def. 1*

wash

1 To **wash** is to clean with soap and water: *Be sure to* **wash** *your hands before dinner. It is his turn to* **wash** *the dishes.*

2 A **wash** is a bundle of dirty clothes that needs to be washed: *Put your jeans and socks in the* **wash.**

word

1 A **word** is a sound or group of sounds that means something. We speak **words** when we talk.

2 A **word** is also the written or printed letters that stand for a word: *This page is filled with* **words** *that I can read.*

3 When you give someone your **word**, you give them a promise.

Yy

young

years

Years are periods of time: *He's been driving a bus for many* **years.** A **year** has twelve months. The new **year** starts on January 1.

young

When something is **young**, it is in the early part of life. **Young** is the opposite of old: *The* **young** *elephant stood near its mother.*

Tested Word List

Unit 4

Hear the Cheers

The Great Ball Game

ago
creature
head
loses
still
team

Birthday Joy

The Best Older Sister

attention
different
important
interesting
secretly
special
told

Treasure Pie

Bruno the Baker

kitchen
large
oven
present
ready
today
wash

Paul Goes to the Ball

The Rooster Who Went to His Uncle's Wedding

able
brook
early
feathers
growl
own
story

Yawning Dawn

Missing: One Stuffed Rabbit

calm
family
finally
gathered
hospital
morning
paper
really

Unit 5

Space Dreams

Man on the Moon

began
circled
Earth
ever
remember
rockets
try

Two Lunches at the Mill

Going to Town

behind
crops
edge
sure
trade
upon
word

A True Boating Family

Riding the Ferry with Captain Cruz

course
deck
dock
steers
things
years

Splash!

Down in the Sea: The Jellyfish

beach
floating
flopped
grow
near
poke

Tex and the Big Bad T. Rex

Let's Go Dinosaur Tracking!

claws
front
giant
helmet
probably
someday
stone

Unit 6

The Clubhouse

Lemonade for Sale

above
few
ice
kept
number
sound

Start Collecting! It's Fun!

The Puddle Pail

castle
crocodile
eight
puddle
road
round
shadows
young

Stone Soup: A Folktale

Stone Soup

add
both
contest
delicious
judges
making
mean
stranger

A Good Idea

Annie's Gifts

also
group
radio
squeaked
though
tried

Wicker School Takes Action

City Green

already
empty
nothing
piece
soil
used

Acknowledgments

Text

Page 18: *The Great Ball Game: A Muskogee Story* by Joseph Bruchac. Text copyright © 1994 by Joseph Bruchac. Illustration copyright © 1994 Susan Roth. Reprinted by permission of Dial Books For Young Readers, a division of Penguin Putnam Inc.

Page 48: From *The Best Older Sister* by Sook Nyul Choi; ill. by Cornelius Van Wright & Ying-Hwa Hu, copyright © 1997 by Sook Nyul Choi. Illustrations copyright © 1997 by Cornelius Van Wright and Ying-Hwa Hu. Used by permission of Random House Children's Books, a division of Random House, Inc.

Page 67: "Seeing a New Sister" from *Feelings, Lines, Colors* by E. Alma Flagg. Reprinted by permission.

Page 78: *Bruno the Baker* by Lars Klinting. Copyright © 1997 by Lars Klinting. Translation copyright © 1997 by Henry Holt and Company, Inc. Reprinted by permission of Henry Holt and Company Inc. and Groundwood/Douglas & Mc Intyre Children's Books, Canada

Page 112: *The Rooster Who Went to His Uncle's Wedding* by Alma Flor Ada. Copyright © 1993 by Alma Flor Ada. Reprinted by permission of G. P. Putnam's Sons, a division of Penguin Putnam Inc.

Page 144: *Missing: One Stuffed Rabbit* by Maryann Cocca-Leffler. Text and illustrations copyright © 1998 by Maryann Cocca-Leffler. Reprinted by permission of Albert Whitman & Company.

Page 171: "Rosie" from *Lunch Money* by Carol Diggory Shields. Copyright © 1995 by Carol Diggory Shields. Reprinted by permission of Dutton Children's Books, a division of Penguin Putnam Inc.

Page 188: *Man on the Moon* by Anastasia Suen. Illustrated by Benrei Huang. Text copyright © 1997 Anastasia Suen. Illustration copyright © 1997 by Benrei Huang. Reprinted by permission of Viking Children's Books, a division of Penguin Putnam Inc.

Page 216: *Going to Town.* Text adapted from *Little House in the Big Woods* by Laura Ingalls Wilder. Illustrated by Renée Graef. Text copyright © 1932 Laura Ingalls Wilder, renewed © 1959 by Roger Lea MacBride. "Little House" ® is a registered trademark of HarperCollins Publishers, Inc. Illustrations copyright © 1995 by Renée Graef. Reprinted by permission of HarperCollins Publishers.

Page 240: *A True Boating Family* © 1998 David McPhail.

Page 246: *Riding the Ferry with Captain Cruz* by Alice K. Flanagan. Text copyright © 1996 Childrens Press, Inc., a Division of Grolier Publishing Co., Inc. All rights reserved. Reprinted by permission.

Page 257: "Barcarola"/"The Boatman's Song" by Nicolás Guillén from *Por El Mar De Las Antillas Anda Un Barco De Papel*, Lóguez Ediciones. Ctra de Madrid, 90.

Page 268: *Down in the Sea: The Jellyfish* by Patricia Kite. Text copyright © 1993 by L. Patricia Kite. Reprinted by permission of Albert Whitman & Company.

Page 296: From *Let's Go Dinosaur Tracking!* by Miriam Schlein. Copyright © 1991 by Miriam Schlein. Reprinted by permission of the author.

Page 313: "Strange Footprints" by Vivian Gouled. Reprinted by permission.

Page 330: *Lemonade for Sale* by Stuart J. Murphy. Text copyright © 1998 by Stuart Murphy. Illustrations copyright © Tricia Tusa. MathStart ™ is a Trademark of HarperCollins Publishers, Inc. Reprinted by permission.

Page 355: "Lemonade for Sale" from *Mummy Took Cooking Lessons* by John Ciardi. Text copyright © 1990 by Judith C. Ciardi. Illustrations copyright © 1990 by Houghton Mifflin Company. Reprinted by permission.

Page 366: *The Puddle Pail* by Elisa Kleven. Copyright © 1997 by Elisa Kleven. Reprinted by permission of Dutton Children's Books, a division of Penguin Putnam Inc.

Page 398: "Stone Soup" from *Kid City Magazine,* November 1994. Copyright 1994 Children's Television Workshop (New York, New York). All rights reserved.

Page 409: "Spaghetti! Spaghetti!" from *Rainy Rainy Saturday* by Jack Prelutsky. Text copyright © 1980 by Jack Prelutsky. Used by permission of HarperCollins Publishers.

Page 420: *Annie's Gifts* by Angela Shelf Medearis. Text copyright © 1994 by Angela Shelf Medearis. Illustrations copyright © 1994 by Anna Rich. All rights reserved. Reprinted by permission of Just Us Books Inc.

Page 441: "Remember" from *It's Raining Laughter* by Nikki Grimes. Text copyright © 1997 by Nikki Grimes. Reprinted by permission.

Page 452: *City Green* by DyAnne DiSalvo-Ryan. Copyright © 1994 by DyAnne DiSalvo-Ryan. Used by permission of HarperCollins Publishers.

Artists

John Sandford, cover, 180
Jerry Tiritilli, 10, 446–451
Kelly Hume, 12, 216b
Susan L. Roth, 18a, 19–36
Pamela Paulsrud, 18b–c, 38, 48b–c, 56b, 62b, 66b, 456b
Anthony Lewis, 38–41
Anne Sibley O' Brien, 42–47
Yoshi Miyake, 48a, 50–56a, 57–62a, 63–65
Janet Ocwieja, 66a, 170, 235
Lindy Burnett, 67, 258–261
David Austin Clar, 68–71
Susan Swan, 72–77
Lars Klinting, 78–99
Doug Knutson, 101
Anthony Carnabuci, 104, 313
Carolyn Croll, 106–111
Kathleen Kuchera, 112–132
Kathi Ember, 136–139, 176
Helen Lester, 138–143
Maryann Cocca-Leffler, 144–169
Cecily Lang, 145
Laura Ovresat, 174–177, 386–389, 441
Phil Wilson, 178, 310–313, 318
Larry Johnson, 182–189
Benrei Huang, 188–203
Brad Teare, 205, 483b, 486a, 489a, 492a
Margeaux Lucas, 206–209, 355
Miles Hyman, 210–215
Renée Graef, 216–234
Gail Piazza, 236–239
David McPhail, 240–245,495
John Zielinski, 246, 254, 257b, c
Shelly Hehenberger, 257a
Allan Eitzen, 262–267
Valerie A. Kells, 283
Roberta Polfus, 285
Reggie Holladay, 286–289
Bernard Adnet, 290–295
Phil Wilson, 296–312, 488a
David Wenzel, 322a
Eliza Schulte Holliday, 322b
Rosario Valderrama, 324–329
Tricia Tusa, 330a, b, 331–353
Bradley Clark, 354c

Unit 6

Contents

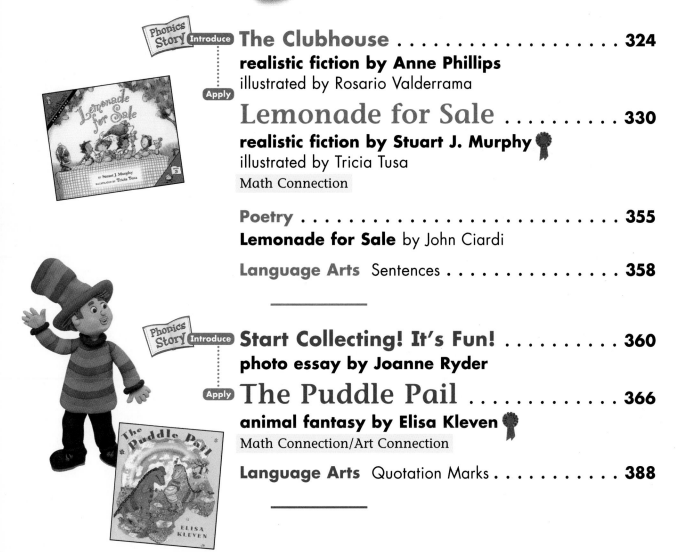

Unit 5

7

Contents

6

Unit 4

5

Contents

Ties Through Time

4

Scott Foresman Reading
My Time to Shine

Program Authors

Peter Afflerbach

James Beers

Camille Blachowicz

Candy Dawson Boyd

Wendy Cheyney

Deborah Diffily

Dolores Gaunty-Porter

Connie Juel

Donald Leu

Jeanne Paratore

Sam Sebesta

Karen Kring Wixson

Scott Foresman

Editorial Offices: Glenview, Illinois • Parsippany, New Jersey • New York, New York
Sales Offices: Parsippany, New Jersey • Duluth, Georgia • Glenview, Illinois
Carrollton, Texas • Ontario, California

About the Cover Artist

Where John Sandford lives in Michigan, there are lots of small animals such as squirrels and chipmunks, but when he is painting an animal, he thinks about a person he knows. He says that thinking of a particular person as he works gives his animals personality.

ISBN 0-328-01816-3

5 6 7 8 9 10 V063 10 09 08 07 06 05 04 03 02

Scott Foresman
Reading
My Time to Shine

My Time to Shine

Ties Through Time

All Aboard!

Just Imagine!

Scott
Foresman